A MAN DEEP
IN MENDIP

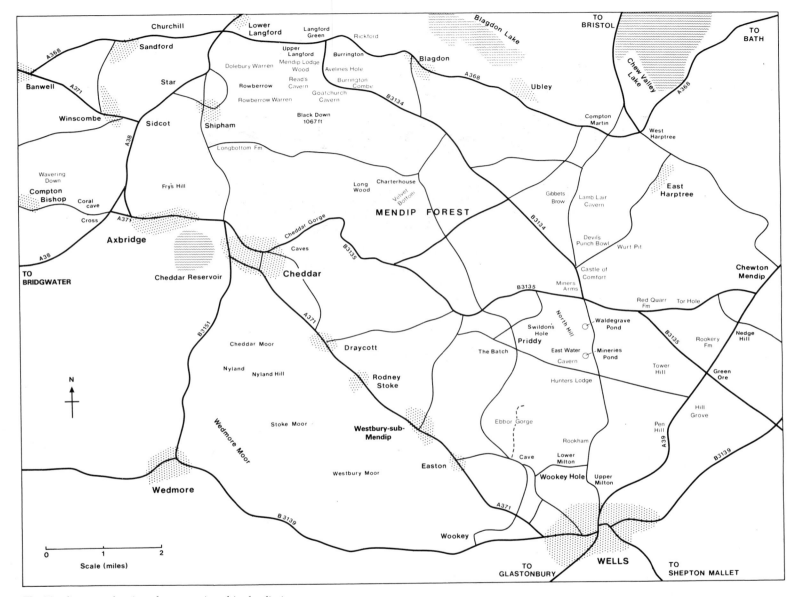

The Mendip area, showing places mentioned in the diaries

A MAN DEEP
IN MENDIP

The Caving Diaries of Harry Savory 1910–1921

Edited by JOHN SAVORY

ALAN SUTTON · GLOUCESTER
SOUTHERN ILLINOIS UNIVERSITY PRESS · CARBONDALE

ALAN SUTTON PUBLISHING
BRUNSWICK ROAD · GLOUCESTER · UK
SOUTHERN ILLINOIS UNIVERSITY PRESS · CARBONDALE · USA

First published in UK 1989
First published in USA 1990

British Library Cataloging in Publication Data

Savory, John, *1943–*
A man deep in Mendip.
1. Somerset Mendip region caves history
I. Title
551.4′47′0942383

UK ISBN 0-86299-567-1

Library of Congress Cataloging in Publication Data applied for

USA ISBN 0-8093-1623-4

Typesetting and origination by
Alan Sutton Publication Limited
Scanning by Spa Graphics Ltd, Cheltenham
Printed in Great Britain by
Dotesios Printers Limited

CONTENTS

ACKNOWLEDGEMENTS

I would like to express my sincere thanks to Wells Museum and the University of Bristol Spelaeological Society, and particularly to Chris Hawkes and Trevor Shaw of those respective organisations, for their friendly cooperation and patience in allowing me to make use here of my father's photographic material in their possession. I am also very grateful to the following: Ethel Plowright (née Balch) and John Balch, for permission to reproduce writings, a pen drawing and surveys of Wookey Hole and Eastwater by their late father, Herbert Balch. William Stanton, for permission to quote from his *Pioneer Under the Mendips* and to reproduce his survey of Gough's Cave. Chris Howes, for printing some of the photographs and for agreeing to write the Foreword to this book. Jaqueline Mitchell, senior editor at Alan Sutton Publishing Ltd., for all her hard work in the planning and preparation of the book. My mother Dorothy Savory, brother Geoff Savory and sister Philippa Perks, for providing information about my father's past. Finally, my wife Eileen, for her cheerful support and help in checking proofs.

3 August 1922. Swildon's Hole: central group, November 12 1921 Grotto (now Tratman's Temple); half-plate

FOREWORD

I have before me a pinewood box, stained with age. Opening it, I am faced with a double row of glass plates, each contained in a yellowed paper envelope. These are stamped with one of J.H. Savory's two addresses at 4 Rodney Place, or Park Row Studios, Bristol, and carry his handwritten captions for the images within. This chest is one part of the Savory material held by Wells Museum; yet more resides with his old club, the University of Bristol Spelaeological Society, the whole collection representing a wealth of historical information that I have personally found fascinating for many years.

Harry Savory was an unusual man, possessing extraordinary skills. There can be no claim to his being the first photographer to venture underground, for numerous subterranean pictures had been taken around the world throughout the latter half of the nineteenth century. Nevertheless, attitudes towards caves had been changing, and the concept of exploration as a sport rather than as a facet of science was a recent one in Britain. Of the many cavers who attempted to produce photographs of the underworld in this new era, Savory was without equal.

Cave photography in the years before World War One was a very different proposition from the techniques of today. By comparison, equipment was crude, and anyone wishing to transport and use it underground in locations like Swildon's Hole had to possess a great deal of determination.

Cavers normally dressed in old clothes, and had to expect a thorough soaking when they entered a swallet cave in a cast-off threadbare jacket. There were no neoprene wet-suits, or waterproof oversuits, for combating the cold. Neither were there any helmets or convenient lights. Herbert Balch, Savory's companion for many years, considered a candle the most useful lighting for caving. This was termed his 'beady eye', or Balch's Dependable Illuminant: B.D.I. Not all cavers agreed, and acetylene lamps attached to cloth caps or trilbys were also in use.

Photography in 1910, when Savory began his underground work, was also undergoing change. Flexible film, similar to modern material, had been introduced along with cheaper more portable cameras, as an alternative to using heavy glass plates. However, most photographers shunned the poorer results this gave, and continued with their wooden cameras supported by a large, cumbersome, tripod. Savory was no exception, placing his need for quality above that of convenience. His camera often suffered in the process, for water could warp the moving parts, and the dark slides which carried the plates would bind in their runners. Nevertheless, flashlight was the greatest problem which had to be overcome.

There were several choices for photographic lighting, all of which Savory made use of. The commonest was some form of magnesium, either as wire, ribbon, or mixed with chemicals to produce flashpowder. Although magnesium weighed little and could be easily transported, it had one major disadvantage with its production of copious fumes. These prevented more than one picture being taken at a time, and on one resourceful occasion Savory even resorted to using fans on bamboo poles to try to clear the air.

Additionally, there were dangers with its use. Flashpowder, one of Savory's standard illuminants, was produced by mixing magnesium powder with an oxidising agent such as potassium chlorate. These could be purchased as a pair of reagents in two separate tins, ready for mixing, although for cost reasons many photographers bought bulk supplies and prepared their own compound. The problem was in keeping the powder dry while mixing it in the cave, or transporting the ready-made flashpowder. Once the oxidising agent was added, an explosive was formed that had roughly twice the power of gunpowder, and accidents were not uncommon. Above ground, where the mixture could be used with relative ease, people had lost limbs and even lives when the powder was treated without caution. How much more difficult its use would have been underground.

By comparison with Savory, today's photographers have a far easier time. Flashbulbs were introduced in 1929, which removed the problems of smoke and fumes, although it took many years before the increased cost was fully accepted. Electronic flash has reduced the cost of artificial light, and slave units (devices that fire remote flashguns without the need for intervening cables) have even avoided the use of tripods. Now, it would be usual to repeat a picture several times in the hope that one exposure would be viable; Savory had to estimate all the factors of distance, aperture, the quantity of magnesium to use with his insensitive plates, and where to place it, as well as his composition, with only one chance to get it right. A trip to Swildon's Sump 1 today might take only a couple of hours, including taking a few photographs, a far cry from the ten hours or so that Savory was sometimes forced to spend underground while recording original cave exploration.

That Savory succeeded so well is a lasting testimony to his professional approach and expertise. Despite the problems, his photographs are still regarded as some of the finest ever produced. His pictures of Mendip have for many years been reproduced in publications without any indication of the difficulties he encountered in their production. Indeed, how many thousands of tourists have bought the low quality postcards of Gough's Cave that Savory produced, on sale for about twenty years, without knowing what quality was contained in the original photographs, or even who had taken them?

I first came across Savory's work while researching my own interest in the development and history of underground photography, and from that time have held his photographic skills in the highest regard. Having now reprinted most of his plate negatives that are still in existence, a task taking many hours, I feel a certain affinity for the images he created, and a double honour for not only being able to work with his original material, but also to be invited to write this Foreword. It is especially interesting, therefore, to see so many pictures reproduced together in this volume, and to be able to read the diary entries that detail how they were taken.

Place yourself in Savory's position. He was a working man, exploring Mendip at weekends and during holidays; a man with an overwhelming interest in his surroundings, a deep desire to record what he saw to the limits of his ability. The detail of his personal writing, which he never thought would be shared with others, enables the reader to partake again in the exploration of Mendip's caves, the rambles across a countryside that has changed in the intervening years. There would have been the anticipation of developing the plates, finding which of the hard-won negatives might produce the required print; the walk back across the fields, carrying a heavy load. You can almost feel the mist rolling over the limestone landscape, or imagine you can see the stars on a crisp night, and enjoy the sweet smell of grass after a long expedition underground.

For me, Savory was one of the masters of underground photography, and his work has rarely been surpassed. I hope that you, too, are as enthralled by the writing and photographs presented in this volume, and with the details of the different world they bring, as I have been.

Chris Howes, FRPS

22 February or April 1913. Gough's Cave: a group of reflected pillars of pure white near the parting of the ways; whole-plate

INTRODUCTION

My father, James Henry Savory (JHS), or Harry as he liked to be known, was a skilled photographer who used to give illustrated lectures on his many varied interests, which included the Mendip hills and Mendip caves. Over a lifetime he accumulated much in the way of prints, negatives and lantern slides, together with related literature. After his death in June 1962, most of the material concerning Mendip went to Wells Museum and the University of Bristol Spelaeological Society; seven albums of prints, the lantern slides and glass plate negatives of Mendip above ground to the former, and negatives of the caves to the latter. For several years afterwards there was talk of producing a book on the caving photographs, but, although some did feature in the *Pictorial History of Swildon's Hole*, a limited edition published by the Wessex Cave Club in 1975, and in the 1977 edition of the *Mendip Cave Guide*, nothing specific was done. It was only in 1985, when I discovered at my mother's home a set of four notebooks comprising JHS's Mendip diary for the period 1910 to 1921, that it became apparent that here was historical material that could be combined with a selection of the photographs to form a book.

JHS was born one hundred·years ago on 25 August 1889, eldest child in a family of four boys and three girls, above a shop in Black Jack Street, Cirencester, where his great-grandfather had been a cabinet maker, and where his grandfather had started a printing and publishing business carried on by his father, Ernest. In 1895, using a steam press, they published Savory's 'Eclipse' series of county maps. The following year Ernest moved with his wife Frances (née Young) and growing family to Bristol in order to expand the business. While new premises were being built in Park Row, he lived and worked in a house in Leigh Woods, and then moved to Rodney Place, Clifton when Park Row Studios were completed. The company was called E. W. Savory Ltd and specialised in fine art work, mainly greetings cards. A sister company, Vandyck Printers Ltd, was also founded by Ernest Savory at about the same time, and this specialised in lower quality work at lower cost for bulk orders.

As well as attracting local business, Ernest travelled extensively in Europe in search of customers, and this allowed him to indulge in his passions for painting and collecting antiques. He was a gifted artist, mainly of architectural subjects, a member of the Royal West of England Academy, and had work exhibited at the Paris Salon. He was also a member of Bristol Council and first Chairman of its Housing Committee.

JHS and his brothers, Richard (Dick, b. 1892), Mortimer (b. 1896) and Bryan (b. 1904), were all educated at Clifton College, where JHS's main sporting interests appear to have been rowing and rifle shooting. Although he would have preferred to become a farmer, this was not to be, because it was still expected then that sons should enter the family business; and so JHS, and later Dick and Mortimer, joined their father at Park Row Studios after leaving school. All three elder brothers were Engineers in the local (Territorial Army) Volunteer Reserve. After World War I, however, Dick eventually did take up farming, when he left to go to South America and then Kenya, and Bryan joined the Colonial Service in Tanganyika. Of JHS's sisters, Helen (b. 1890) died in 1921 while a nurse in London, Frances (b. 1894) became headmistress of York High School for Girls, and Margaret (b. 1897) was a doctor in Hampshire.

JHS inherited his father's artistic interests and soon joined the Bristol Savages, a club for artists. It is not known how his interests in photography, archaeology and natural history arose, however, and nowhere in his diaries is there any indication of how he was introduced to caving or to the people he caved with. An uncle of his, another Mortimer Savory, was a professional photographer in Cirencester, so there may well have been a family influence there. Perhaps his interest in country matters was heightened by an awareness that he was

committed to working in a city environment, and that his youthful ambition of more 'exciting' employment as a farmer was going to be frustrated. For some years after leaving school, he cycled regularly to a farm near Cirencester to help on summer weekends. One can only speculate that it may have been *The Netherworld of Mendip*, which had been written jointly by Ernest Baker and Herbert Balch and published in 1907, or perhaps attendance at a lecture on the subject, that sparked his interest in the Mendip scene.

Herbert Ernest Balch was very much the leading figure in Mendip caving when JHS began to visit the area in 1910. Twenty years older than JHS, Balch was born in 1869 in Wells, where he worked for the Post Office

Dick (R.N.), Harry (J.H.) and Mortimer (E.M.) Savory, c. 1913–14

and lived all his life. By the turn of the century he had already established a reputation as being *the* authority on Mendip caves and their associated archaeology, and even a miraculous escape from almost certain death in about 1900, when his lifeline parted during the 65 ft (winch) descent of the Great Chamber in Lamb Lair Cavern, did not deter him. He helped to found the Wells Natural History and Archaeology Society (WNHAS) in 1888, founded Wells Museum in 1895 to house his own growing collections, and was a popular lecturer in the area. As well as their home in Wells, he and his wife had holiday accommodation at Rookham, on the hill above Wells, which provided an ideal base for his activities on the Mendip plateau. In his youth, the only extensive cave systems known on Mendip were Wookey Hole, where archaeological excavations at the Hyaena Den by Professor Boyd Dawkins had started in 1859, Goatchurch Cavern at Burrington Combe, where excavations by W. Beard had started about 1830, Cox's and (old) Gough's Caves at Cheddar, and Lamb Lair Cavern near West Harptree. All, except the last one, either have been or still are show caves in part. Then in 1898 the magnificent Gough's (new) Cave was opened to the public, and the 'Cheddar Man' skeleton was uncovered there in 1903. In 1901 two younger friends of Balch, Robert Troup and Frank Hiley, broke into Swildon's Hole swallet at Priddy, and a year later, after considerable digging, Balch himself and Harry Willcox finally entered the boulder ruckle at nearby Eastwater swallet to discover the cavern beyond.

In 1906, the first true caving club on the Mendips was formed, the Mendip Nature Research Club, which became the Mendip Nature Research Committee (MNRC) of the WNHAS when the two societies merged in 1908. It was to the MNRC that Balch and Baker, co-authors of *The Netherworld of Mendip*, both belonged, and it was to this group that JHS became affiliated when his caving started in 1910. Clearly his interests coincided with, and were stimulated by, the whole range of MNRC activities.

Ernest Baker was the same age as Balch, but, though born in Bath, was never based permanently in Somerset during his caving career. He began caving in 1900 in the Peak District while living in Derby, joined the Yorkshire Ramblers Club, and subsequently explored all the main caving areas in Derbyshire, Yorkshire, Somerset and Ireland. He moved to live in Cheshire in 1904 and London in 1906. After a visit to the Mendips in 1902, Balch invited him to join in cave exploration there, and from 1903 onwards he was a regular participant, usually renting accommodation locally. A librarian by profession, he was awarded the degree of Doctor of Literature in 1908, and he wrote numerous books on caving, climbing and academic subjects. Like Balch, therefore, he was a remarkable man, who did more than anyone else to promote caving as a sport and to bring cavers in different areas into contact with each other.

The other 'regulars' amongst JHS's caving companions were mainly local men: Robert Troup, who played a major part in exploring and surveying Swildon's Hole and Eastwater; Ernest Barnes, who later became Mayor of Wells; Balch's youngest brother,

Reginald; Paul Sinnock, Stanley Wheeler, Holly and Webb. Baker's friend Harold Kentish also made an important contribution in Eastwater, but he was killed in action at Amiens in March 1918. Later there were Eric Bird and Clement Richardson, and 'Bristol men' like Jack Brownsey, Reginald Read and Edgar Tratman.

In the early years caving was seen more as a serious science than as a sport, and exploration was usually undertaken with a view to shedding new light on archaeology, hydrology and geomorphology. Also, although relatively few caves had been opened up on Mendip, Balch and the others were fully aware that there was much more to discover. This may explain why so much of JHS's time was spent above ground, looking for signs of old mining activity, burial mounds and sink-holes, and digging at swallets and in some of the smaller holes in the hope of breaking into new systems. Below ground, the explorers took care to survey everything they discovered, and in this JHS came to play an active role.

Compared with today, these early caving expeditions were major undertakings, involving much planning, heavy equipment, and usually taking many hours. There were no specialised clothing or helmets, a cloth cap or trilby being used to protect the head, and hand-held candles were usually used in preference to the large acetylene lamps, electric lighting not coming in till much later. Hot meals were often prepared in the caves, in which case cooking gear also had to be taken down. The hemp ropes, rope ladders, pulleys, etc. were much bulkier than modern light-weight materials, some

equipment had to be protected from jarring, some to be kept dry, and if excavation was intended there were heavy digging tools as well. On top of all this, for photography, there were plate cameras, glass plates, tripods and materials for illumination.

Before JHS began photographing in Mendip caves, the only others to have done so with much success were Harry Bamforth and Herbert Balch himself. The former was from Holmfirth in Yorkshire, and had already earned a reputation for excellent cave photography when he first came to Mendip with Ernest Baker, at Balch's invitation, in March 1903. Photographs

Equipment required for a day in Eastwater or elsewhere

taken by him in all the main Mendip caves of the time appear in JHS's albums, and, since there is no mention of him in JHS's diaries, it seems likely that these were taken before 1910. Most of Balch's photography had been in Wookey Hole, Lamb Lair and Eastwater, but he appears to have been quite happy to hand over the responsibility of camera work to JHS, because there is only occasional reference to photography by him in the diaries. Other cave photographs in JHS's albums were taken by Baker, Sinnock, McEwan the Wookey Hole guide, and Dawkes and Partridge, professional photographers from Wells.

JHS's earliest cave photographs were taken with a quarter-plate ($4\frac{1}{4}$in × $3\frac{1}{4}$in) camera, but subsequently most were in half-plate ($6\frac{1}{2}$in × $4\frac{3}{4}$in) and some in whole-plate ($8\frac{1}{2}$in × $6\frac{1}{2}$in). Unfortunately, there is very little detail in the diaries about the equipment he used, or about the preparation and processing of the glass plates, and whether or not he did any of this himself. He certainly had Sanderson and Thornton Pickard plate cameras later on, but, judging from their immaculate condition, these were never used for cave photography. He usually took just one camera into a cave at a time, although occasionally two, and perhaps six or twelve plates prepared for exposure. Since only a few photographs could be taken, great care was needed in planning each exposure. The picture was composed while the scene was illuminated with candle or acetylene light, and then, having arranged camera and tripod accordingly, the photographer exposed the plate for as long as necessary while his assistant(s) provided

illumination with magnesium ribbon, flash powder or limelight, or a combination of these. Special effects could be obtained by using more than one light source, behind the camera and at the side or in front, but always out of sight. Furthermore, very long exposures were required with limelight, since photographic emulsion is less sensitive to it than to magensium light, so one person could move round highlighting different parts of a large chamber with flash powder or ribbon while the shutter was open, and could even include himself repeatedly in the picture if so desired. The disadvantage of long exposures was that human subjects had to maintain rigid poses in order to avoid being blurred, and if candles moved in the picture these left tracks which then had to be masked on either the negative or the print. In addition, there was often much fuming after long exposures, and so if more photographs were required, the photographer had to wait each time for the atmosphere to clear. Photography thus contributed greatly to the duration of early expeditions.

Despite the somewhat primitive conditions, JHS generally achieved remarkably good results, even by today's standards, and the pictures selected for this book represent a cross-section of his best work. Most have been reprinted from the original glass negatives, and no attempt has been made to remove blemishes, from either 'silvering', scratches or the candle tracks referred to above, in the few cases where they appeared. The diary entries, also, have been selected and edited in such a way as to emphasize the book's caving theme.

Photography in the streamway above the lower water chamber, Swildon's Hole; drawing by John Hassall dated 4 October 1913 from a sketch by JHS (see diary 17 April 1911)

22 February or April 1913. Gough's Cave: the Fonts, not far from the entrance; whole-plate

1910

JHS's first recorded visit to a Mendip cave was to Eastwater Cavern with Balch, Kentish, Sinnock and Troup on 4 June 1910, when he was twenty years old. That this was also his first caving expedition, apart from 'twice at Wookey Hole' on unspecified dates, is confirmed in the entry for 8 April 1912.

EASTWATER 4 June 1910 (Saturday)

I went down to Wells on the Friday evening and was met by Balch and Sinnock at the station. After paying a call at Troup's we at once started for Baker's bungalow at Rookham. Arrived at the bungalow about dusk and soon after Kentish, who had been there two nights, was seen on the road below pushing his bike up. He had been making purchases for the following day.

We were up betimes on the following morning (Saturday) making preparations for the day. Balch and Troup had to come up from Wells and we were to meet them at the cave mouth. I made a beeline across the moor while the other two cycled round by road. We left what things we did not want at a farm nearby and then, assembling at the cave mouth, donned our boiler suits and were ready with the kit to descend at 10

a.m. Balch and Troup went first, myself following with the others behind again. We had lit our candles before starting. As soon as we were all under way, forming a chain, we passed down the kit which comprised ropes, picks, entrenching tools, compasses, aneroid, food and cooking gear etc. When this was settled we each passed down that much further and handed on again, and so on until we reached the head of the 380 ft Way. Here we left all the food etc. and continued each with some article comparatively easily down to the foot of the Way. Here there were two ways, both 'choked' to the top, and we at once set to work on the right, having determined that this one would be more profitable in order to find a continuation of the 380 ft Way. The one to the left did not look so important and was a much lower arch, being filled with a very compact choke in which many large stones had lodged. The water, also, appeared to drain to the right so we chose the latter (10.50). Only one could work at the choke at a time so we took this job in turn, the remainder laboriously passing back all the excavated earth, first of all bridging the streamlet with large stones in order not to stop the stream or to wash choke back again. We worked hard till about 1.15 p.m.

but still no sign of the end of the choke. We then returned 50 ft to the chamber at the head of the 380 ft Way, Kentish and myself starting first, to get the food ready. We collected water from the pools and soon had a large pot of splendid pea soup (made from condensed soup) steaming over an alpine spirit stove in an alpine kettle. The others had arrived by now so we started on this, going on to sandwiches, biscuits and chocolate. We also had a Thermos of coffee which was smashed on the way up.

After a short rest we resumed work and continued till about 4 p.m. There was now no need for handing back so far so we left Balch and Sinnock at work and returned to the head of the 380 ft Way, starting on the passage eastward which leads through a series of canyons and bedding caves, leading first south-east then north to the 100 ft aven [high rift passage]. We explored passages leading away beyond this to a distance of about 40 ft. Kentish pushed on furthest here, the branches beyond the saddle were only seen by him. The cairn in the cavern immediately south of the aven was made by him on a previous occasion when that (cairn) was the furthest point reached. We three then made our way back. I found that it was particularly tight in getting round the big stalagmite. One has to be careful not to miss this spot for turning off, as the cave extends a great way to the S. and S.E. here and one cannot travel W. below the line of wedged stones. We returned to the others by 6 p.m., and by 6.30 with a final shove at the back of the choke with his foot, Balch sent the last of it down a 40° slope on the further side. The slope was composed (on the surface at least) with coke material probably washed down on previous occasions and some of course now. We could see but a few feet ahead so Kentish was roped up and slid feet foremost down the slope, each of us paying out rope from above. The way led round to the right and he soon reached a point where he could dispense with the rope and where his movements were more free. Then we each in turn slid down in any manner we liked.

We found ourselves in a 20 ft rift cavern about 5 ft across and with a large mud soak at the further end. This seemed to be the end of any visible watercourse in this tunnel (except perhaps with extensive floods) as a few yards further on we came to the face of a vertical choke 9 ft high. Above the mud soak, in which we sank over our boots, there were the remains of flood matter (from the last flood) up to a height of 6 or 7 ft. Probably if this mud was excavated we should find crevices large or small through which water brought to a stop by the 9 ft choke finds a further outlet. Above the choke, the ceiling running roughly at the same height, was a very narrow rift 12–15 in wide with just enough room for two men, so that Kentish still leading was hoisted up by us, Balch following. These two started squeezing through and pushed on for about 21 ft, where the rift widened a little. Just beyond some stones wedged near the floor was a small pot and here abruptly finished this passage, but just before this, running at right angles to the right, was a second rift with a drop not of 9 ft but 15 ft. The depth Kentish was unable to see, so we passed the rope along the mud soak the length of the narrow rift to him. He was then let down, touching bottom at 15 ft. This was not an extensive rift, 15 ft long only, and bar some small rifts and cracks on each side and some small soaks in the floor, there was nothing more of interest and no further means of progress this way. The last mentioned point was the lowest reached that day, about 190 ft below surface, we had not aimed at attaining a great depth. After hauling Kentish up we all started skywards.

Just below the original choke was my tightest squeeze of the day, for although the rift was quite high here, its width was so narrow that with my arms pinned to my sides and my head fixed in one direction I had only my toes to lever myself up with, and being a steep slope easy to slide down it was far from easy to push up. At last I reached the mouth and with a final heave the man in front of me pulled me into the foot of the 380 ft Way where we had been working all the morning. From there up to the top of the way it was easy. At the top we had our tea and then started our tedious climb up to the open air. I was still more impressed with the ease with which one might lose oneself among these huge irregular boulders. We reached the mouth a little before 9 p.m. and I experienced to the full the feelings described by Mr Balch of coming up to the open sky after a lengthy stay and hard work in cramped quarters underground. We went to the farm and after getting our coats started for the bungalow forthwith. Again I took a line across the moor, it was very mysterious in the dark. Reaching the bungalow I changed from my clothes which had soon been torn to rib-bons. We then had a good meal, turning in early after making sundry notes and sketches.

In August 1910, further exploration near Kentish's Cairn in Eastwater revealed an important link which completed the Traverse connecting the 380 ft Way – so called because its (then) lower end choke point was along 380 ft of passageway from the cave's entrance – with the top of the Canyon. Only a week or two after this discovery, on 28 August, it enabled a party of Army officers led by Baker and Troup to bypass extreme flood-water conditions in the Boulder Chamber, brought on by prolonged heavy rain, that would otherwise have blocked their exit from the cave. This is the incident referred to in the entry for 8 April 1912. The same rains, which caused the worst flooding on Mendip for many years, also washed the 9 ft vertical choke at the bottom of the 380 ft Way entirely away, allowing clear access to a lower chamber.

JHS did not take a camera to Eastwater, or on his next caving trip to Cox's and Gough's show caves at Cheddar on 2 December. He did, however, purchase photographic illustrations at the latter two, which may well have inspired him to try for himself. The first mention of a camera is the 'T.S. quarter-plate' that he took on a short holiday after Christmas when he stayed two nights with Troup in Wells. Although this does not correspond with any mass-produced camera, it could have been a privately made (wooden) model, many of which were then still in use. He does not mention photography on the first day's caving,

22 February or April 1913. Gough's Cave: bacon rasher curtains and pencil stalactites; whole-plate

27 December, when he and others led by Balch explored new parts of the Upper Series in Swildon's Hole, but took his first cave photographs in Wookey Hole the following day.

CHEDDAR 2 December 1910

I went down to Cheddar at midday on Saturday in order to visit Cox's and Gough's Caves. At this time a period of very heavy rains was just coming to an end, and miles of country round Yatton and Congresbury were under water and also a stretch in the Glastonbury direction. I went straight to Cox's Cavern and proceeded with the guide over all the parts open to the public and also a short way into the new passage which it is proposed to excavate beyond the last Rift Chamber. The prospects are that more beautiful stalactite scenery will be discovered there. The acetylene gas is very successful throughout and all unsightly pipes are concealed, and though not so liable to floods as the cavern above, a very efficient pumping system keeps Cox's Cave free from flood water. I purchased a very representative collection of illustrations, and learnt that the beautiful colouring of the stalagmite which is the great feature of this cavern is due to the following: pure white which occurs but rarely is due to deposits of pure calcite of lime (aragonite?), red to iron, dull grey and translucent black to lead, dull black to black oxide of manganese. A great amount of excavation has been done to render an easy passage for the public, many fine stalactites being damaged in so doing, but these have all been repositioned with plaster.

I then proceeded to Gough's Cave, going in a little way with one of the Gough brothers. Here the river has not as yet left the rocks, and the consequence is that all the lower parts of the cave are deeply flooded, cutting off the passage. No pump I think could possibly deal with it. Shortly before my visit the water had reached the roof in the first big dip, but now it had dropped enough to hear the rushing of the falls beyond, although one could go no further than the dip. I examined the skeleton of the Neolithic man and also the spot where it was discovered. This cavern is illuminated with electric light. Here again I purchased photographs and a freshly cut piece of stalagmite.

I then walked about a mile and a half up the gorge, admiring its beautiful scenery. It seems endless and several miles must be done before one ceases to see the rocks at each side of the roadway. I returned to the Cliff Hotel for tea, in the gardens of which one sees to advantage the volume and velocity of the water which but a few yards further up the road first sees daylight. It leaves the cliffs in two streams, one smaller than the other and but a short distance apart. These, however, almost at once join to form a single stream.

SWILDON'S HOLE 27 December 1910

I arrived [at Wells] at 10.30 p.m. after picking up Sinnock at Yatton. Balch and Troup met us at the station and we at once turned in. I had taken down food for three meals together with a spirit stove, also camera (T.S. quarter-plate), stand and flashlight. I took 30 ft and 60 ft 2-in ropes as theirs had not lately been tested, and hired a bicycle from Barnes for the two days. The next morning broke with splendid sunlight weather and a crisp frost. We were astir betimes and the whole party was ready to start up at 10.05 a.m., Balch, Troup, two Barnes, Sinnock, Savory and two others [one was Wheeler]. We arrived at Priddy at 11.10 a.m., left our coats, bikes etc. at the farm and proceeded to the cave mouth. Although the water had been drained out of the dam by releasing the plug early in the morning, we found that there was far too much water running down to allow us to enter, so that for some time we were delayed, trying to find a means of entrance. Two or three started trying to excavate the hole on the left (entrance in the roots of an ash), and although afterwards we could see lights through in the main passage, the fissures were far too small for progress and impossible to enlarge. We had noticed that drainage seemed to tend slightly towards a little bay on the right, and after damming the water off from this we excavated a great deal of mud, loose stone etc. with spade and bar. Even when we appeared to have got down to bed rock I managed to lever up several large stones round the mouth of the little swallow hole that had made its appearance. This enabled that passage to take perhaps treble the amount of water that it had taken before being disturbed, but even now the flow down the main passage through the dam was not decreased to any marked extent. It was still impossible. We had had no rain for nearly a week but there was still a great amount of water on the surface.

At that point we had lunch. We now came to the conclusion that the only thing to do was to stop the dam and while it was filling to make descents, leaving a man at the top to give us warning when the water was getting near the top. Balch went down nearly 60 ft and found that the S bend was tightly and completely choked. This of course up to then was the usual route taken. The water when flowing down was subdivided about the portion of the rock, taking many small passages and joining again below together with the stream from the right. Down below we could hear the deep rumbling of a waterfall below the choke. We started methodically to pick the choke to pieces, forming a chain and handing right back to the entrance or packing securely in side rifts. It was composed of stones not only small but large boulders as well, which must have had great force behind them to move them, and also a huge amount of fresh weed from the dam, all crevices filled up with mud. We emptied the dam three times having, say, about forty minutes between each, and with these repeated sudden swillings of water, together with our excavation, three passages made themselves seen: 1. the old S bend, 2. a small vertical drop immediately at the entrance to the above, 3. a horizontal fissure running off to the left from just above the vertical drop. By means of an acetylene lamp we could see a very promising boulder chamber beyond this, but by this time we had to go up. By kicking away wedged stones and silt from the entrance to the horizontal fissure, sufficient room was made for passage.

Our original intention had been before

descending to enlarge a fissure, though not the above, to render a passage downward easier than the S bend. However, on discovering this fissure we gave up the former idea. We let all the water out and made our chain as before, but this time to clear the entrance of passage to the left. This was not a long job and when complete we all worked up to the surface again. We were now going to penetrate into this new passage. A party of four was chosen – Balch, Sinnock, Wheeler and myself – while the others were stationed at intervals up to the surface to give us timely warning. We took the 30 ft rope and reached the chamber in front of the S bend, where Balch roped up and pushed through the small new passage. After about 12 ft there was an abrupt fall of about 5 ft, leading into a roomy boulder chamber. It was easy to pass through and drop into this chamber, but difficult to return because there was no hold whatsoever and it was necessary to get a push up from behind in order to get a first hold into the little hole 5 ft up in the side of the chamber. This chamber, as mentioned, was quite roomy, about 12 ft by 8 ft and 6 ft high. The floor was absolutely covered with boulders of all sizes, but mostly small; one huge square one just like a table had apparently fallen square right into the middle of the floor, about 4 ft by 3 ft. On entering the chamber the floor sank away to the left, the stones getting larger and covering up what seemed to be two low recesses or passages at each corner at that side. We had no time to examine these but they did not look promising.

Right opposite the entrance were first traces of splash stalagmite. On the right clearly lay our route, both at the far and the near right corners there appeared to be passages downward. The one at the near corner did not look so promising so Balch was roped up, the other three of us taking the rope and he then started feet first through a small vertical hole in the floor. He had got three parts through and was trying to find a foothold where the rocks were very much undercut when the whole of the floor in that corner seemed to give a little, letting down a crowd of stones and starting to move the big wedged stone at the corner on which he had put most of his weight. We pulled him up sharp and after clearing away all loose stones and thoroughly testing the corner stone, we let him down what proved to be a rough vertical drop of about 15 ft. He took a lot of loose stuff down with him. It was a very awkward corner with no holdfast and loose material all around. Sinnock then started down but his hold gave out and he fell most of the way, happily landing on top of Balch and so did not hurt himself. I was next and it was thought better to use the rope again, but when I got half-way through, the stones under me all started to give and I came back. By that time those down below had found the end of the other passage from the near corner and reported that it was much easier, being a slope instead of vertical and similar to a staircase, though very tight. Wheeler and I cleared our end a little and both of us then got down easily. We found ourselves in a very peculiar chamber. It was long with a turning sharp back half-way along on the right, and just beyond this on a little shelf of

22 February or April 1913. Gough's Cave: in the (upper) Boulder Chamber with Niagara Falls on the left; whole-plate

rock was a single stalagmite like a sentinel, thick and stumpy. We went along to the other end where the roof gradually met our heads and found recesses going still further back on the left and right at the end at about head level. These were all covered with splash (as was most of this end) but floor and ceiling seemed to join before very far, though there were some interesting looking corners. Time was getting short, however, and we returned to the branch. This turned sharp back and started at once to go down a sharp slippery gully, the first sign of water on this route; from beyond we could hear the roar of a waterfall. After a little the gully ran diagonally under a square ledge of rock from which poured continually a fringe of water, the near boundary of a chamber we were just about to enter. There was water everywhere, falling water behind us, water pouring in from the original (S bend direction) passages on our right, and dropping everywhere from the roof. Immediately in front of us was a wonderful sight, a twin waterfall (of only a few feet) joining in mid-air then joining other streamlets and flowing away to the left downwards. Of course under flood conditions of any sort the volume would be many times as great, for it must be remembered that practically no water was flowing from the dam, which was stopped. After admiring this for some time we heard a distant shout telling us to come up (6-in left in the dam). We therefore proceeded upwards, all taking my way up into the boulder chamber this time, which was of course a very much easier ascent, and we all reached the open once more. Unfortunately, Balch's little haversack and kit was left by mistake in a corner on our return journey, and was washed away by the next flood. We are hoping to meet it at Wookey Hole one day.

WOOKEY HOLE 28 December 1910

Troup and myself cycled to Wookey Hole with photographic kit at about 10 a.m., where we met Balch, Sinnock and Wheeler. Our main intention was to get a good photo of the third chamber and we went there without loss of time. Some delay was caused in getting set up and focussed as there was much damp in the air and the candles were quite distant. We gave the whole of an Excelsior flash ribbon, but of course it was very local and therefore hopeless. Balch exposed his plate by the side of mine but with no result. Another time it would be far better to illuminate in various places sheltered from the camera and so bring up local features. We then proceeded to the Spur and Wedge where we got a satisfactory photo using ribbon. We did not wait long here but made preparations to start on the upper galleries on the other side. We took another flash of the slope under the doorway with the party on the way up. Balch, who had to go on duty, left us here and we got up into the Grill chamber where Sinnock and myself took a few with ribbon.

Our intention now was to get to the furthest extremity of the higher bedding cave and do some digging. We therefore packed up and leaving everything but the shovels behind started on our way. The way under the Grill did not look very tempting and it was certainly as tight a squeeze as one

28 December 1910. Wookey Hole: Wheeler, Balch, Sinnock and Troup climbing out of the first chamber into the west series; quarter-plate

could wish for, added to which the floor was covered with standing water and moist drip. We all got through after some hard work, all wondering how we had managed it, and we then found ourselves in the vertical rift. There was not much difficulty in climbing this and we came to quite an imposing chamber, very broad, sometimes high enough to sit up in, sometimes rather tight, the floor covered with red earth and the roof of rock meeting the floor here and there as if for support. I did a break back to the right by myself to have a look at some fine stalactites. These were the only ones occurring in this large earth chamber above the rift. There were traces of bones left here and also the floor in some places consists of numerous tightly packed balls. The first points to animal habitation, and some say the second does too? Badgers (traces of which are left) used this cave and gained admittance through a small entrance high up on the cliff face. We were working back now towards this and towards a corner of the earth cave where the sides come close together forming a sort of gully. There was not much headroom now (say average 3 ft) and we were going up a slight incline. At the top of this the sides nearly met, forming a kind of neck going off at right angles and then again widening somewhat. It was here that we had brought our shovels to try and work nearer the surface of the cliff. We did an hour's useful excavation taking turn and turn about. As time was now getting short we started the return journey, the Grill chamber looking more impossible than ever. Starting from the far side it is exceedingly narrow and there are two stalagmite bosses just where you want to begin. We reached the entrance without any further incident, picking up our kit at the door to the upper chambers. Of the photos taken, Spur and Wedge, ropeladder up to new chambers, and one taken in new chambers came out exceedingly well but the third chamber was much underexposed owing to its size.

1911

In 1911 JHS became a member of both the WNHAS and the MNRC, and began to visit Mendip more regularly. There are thirty diary entries for the year, but only nine of them record expeditions into caves. The rest describe exploratory trips, some with a camera and some accompanied by other members of the family, to new areas of interest such as Burrington Combe and Ebbor Gorge, and also a sustained period of digging at Hillgrove Swallet near his new base at Green Ore during the main summer holiday in late August and early September.

The first entries cover the Easter holiday, 15–18 April, when the main expedition was down Swildon's Hole, with cameras, on Easter Monday. As well as this, JHS visited Wookey Hole and took photographs above ground on the Saturday, and cycled up on the hills in the Priddy area again on the Tuesday. During this holiday he stayed in Wells with Mrs Parsons in the High Street, 'now Wickenden Restaurant, a place where they are used to caving men'. Troup, his host in December 1910, had left Wells for Bridgwater and was stopping with Hiley at Ebbor.

WOOKEY HOLE 15 April 1911 (Saturday)

I had to go to Wells on the Saturday before

Easter so as to get in an early start for Swildon's on the Monday. There was nothing else doing so I visited Wookey again where Balch was taking over a party of the Cyclist Touring Club. We did the three main chambers, letting off flares, and on the way back some of us struck off for the Spur and Wedge. A big fat perspiring man was bringing up the rear who was very doubtful about risking his body in such places. However,

Plan and section of Wookey Hole Cavern, by H.E. Balch and R.D.R. Troup, 1912

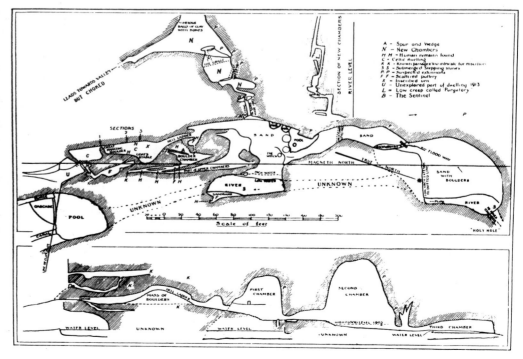

22 February or April 1913. Gough's Cave: the
Organ Pipes in Solomon's Temple; whole-plate

just as the last of us was disappearing round the first corner he finally decided to come. He made a sprint and just got round the corner to see the last of us vanish again. He didn't like this so hurriedly began to go back to the rest of the party. The first thing he did was to drop his candle which promptly went out. He was still out of sight of both parties but continued his mad rush back, barking his shins considerably. He set up a mighty yell for help and we found him when we went back, sitting on a boulder in a beastly funk. We got to the Spur and Wedge and started from here on a route I had not been before, underneath the rocks for just a little while afterwards. There are two ways, the right much narrower than the left, which run parallel and then join again after dipping considerably and rising much more (there was one sheer climb of 15 ft). This passage works round to the right where there is fine conglomerate to be seen, till it reaches the Spur and Wedge passage only a few yards from the main cave. Here we joined the rest of the party and after cleaning up at Adlam's [George Adlam's guest house opposite Wookey Hole Mill], all cycled into Wells and HEB showed us the cathedral.

SWILDON'S HOLE 17 April 1911 (Easter Monday)

The party consisted of HEB [Balch], Troup, Wheeler, Reg Balch, Hope, Barnes, JHS, two farmers, W. Hiley, oldish man? and Webb, twelve in all. We assembled from different points at the mouth at about 9 a.m. It was after a very dry spell of weather and there was much less water going down than at Christmas, beside which we found that the little swallet in the pond to the left of the main hole was taking more water owing to our opening it up previously. We spent the first half-hour in handing up a lot more of the choke stones to the surface, after which all the party except Balch and myself went on down to the grotto by the long dry way, gaining this through the new boulder chamber and slide opened at Christmas 1910.

Balch and I stopped back to improve still further the waterway at the head of the S bend and mouth of the boulder chamber. When Troup got round underneath us at the other end of the S bend, there was a discussion as to its exact locality, Troup saying that the lower end was totally different from what we had imagined it to be from the top. He also said that the top of it was a different place to where we were. This points to an alteration of the position of the boulders during the time that it was choked or else the addition of some more boulders from the stream way. In any case from both ends it presented quite a different appearance to the last time it had been accessible. We worked for some time, clearing the top of the S bend and packing stones and boulders away at the sides. This being done to our satisfaction, we went down through the new chamber, which with the next was much smaller than I first remembered. We passed up to the right of the little twin waterfalls, and after going down one or two streaming wet rifts we gained the long dry way down. All the luggage and food had gone on ahead and we just had our two cameras; we got several good photos and, pursuing our way downwards, soon heard voices far below us.

We joined the rest of the party in the grotto where they had soup on the go and all the food ready.

Of course I had not been into the long dry way before and its beauty struck me as wonderful; it got better and better, ending in the stalactite grotto. This was simply grand. We had a really good time here and after packing up all the things, started downward again through a passage to right of entrance, under a stalagmite bridge. Everywhere was stalagmite of varying colours, but below us we soon heard the waterfalls and very soon the rocks began to show more and more till there was very little of the calcite left. We soon reached the lower chamber and this is very impressive; immediately in front of you as you enter is a deep canal (say 5 or 6 ft) worn in the rocks, and beyond this rises like an island in the middle a huge block of stone and old stalagmite which the water is gradually planing down. Little foothold is given on the near side and it is either a climb down and up again or a judicious jump trusting to get a grip where you land. Balch tried the latter, slipped and fell up to his hips in a pot-hole in the running water, giving himself a bad jar. We all got safely up and this chamber presents a weird sight. Still looking straight ahead, we saw a big rift in the waterworn streaming rocks, and down this poured the stream towards us, now in considerable volume, and in the distance is seen a first fall of 6 or 7 ft (with a very deep pot below it, 5 ft camera stand went in to top without touching bottom), and beyond again curving round from the right is a higher second fall with good pot-hole carving round it. This stream runs here and there through the lower chamber, round each side of the island and down a second rift to right of entrance as you come in.

We scrambled along the rift ahead, straddling it at a height above the water, sadly afraid of going in, and the magnesium ribbon lit up a wonderful sight here. With great pains we set up the camera, digging the legs into the half-rotten rock and just missing the right hand side which is a curve. Got a fairly successful photo, people lighting it with ribbon from above us and beyond, remainder of party took it in turns to see it. We got back in safety to the lower chamber and took another of the entrance of this rift and the stream, showing off to advantage its great height here by placing men at intervals upwards. There seem to be many side passages about here as men were crawling all round during this photo, and one head appeared high above our top man through a hole practically in the roof. This was gained by a side branch to the right of the rift with falls.

Most of the party now prepared to return, but HEB, Troup, Wheeler, Hiley and myself were stopping down for some while longer. We fixed the camera up in the stream way leading out of the chamber and took a photo of the stream itself bearing round to the right under some fine curtains towards the big drop [see drawing, p.xvii]. Balch told me that these curtains used almost to touch the water, but now they have been worn away so that you could scramble underneath them, uncomfortably but without getting wet. After these all stalactites vanish again and we came to

6 April 1912. Swildon's Hole: Barnes senior at the base of 20–30 feet of stalactite in the passage between the Old Grotto and lower water chamber; half-plate

another rift just like the one above. We straddled along this for some way and could hear the roar of the 60 ft drop beyond, bearing round to left again but there was too much water for us to try it, and we did not go quite far enough to see it. Troup has a survey of the cave partly finished. After spending some more time down here we returned to the grotto at about 4 p.m. and again my canteen came in useful as we made some fine coffee from condensed coffee and milk. This was our second meal and after it we packed everything, rubbish included, ready for the return journey. HEB got a very good photo of us other four having tea in the grotto and a fine boss in front of us. I also got a good one in the far end from entrance of Hiley and Wheeler up among the stalactites. We had arranged to be out before dark so that we did not delay long in getting ready, and we chose the short dry way up as being a different route. We took several photos on the way up, among which a stalagmite of coral formation and one of a small pot-hole in working order were good and interesting.

This way is not so grand as the longer route, but is of interest even if with less stalactites. Towards the top no stalactites showed, but where the water had eaten out the limestone it left blackish fossils standing right out. We ended up with a long inclined and narrow rift, which on climbing to the top (15 ft) we found ourselves soon at the foot of the S bend. We got out in good time and found the others all vanished. We walked, a motley crew, to Farmer Main's barn where we changed, packed and returned to Wells. I visited Balch in the evening and we developed some of his plates. Kit on this occasion was quarter-plate T.S. camera, stand, canteen, ropes etc. We found Balch's camera stand top firmly wedged among some rocks where it had been left in the flood last Christmas.

On Whit Tuesday, JHS went by train to Burrington Combe on his own with a Goerz Anschutz half-plate camera. He saw the Rock of Ages, Plumley's Den, Aveline's Hole and walked to the top of Blackdown, returning via the E. Brooklet to have tea at Burrington. On 1 July he returned to Burrington with his father and the Goerz Anschutz, and took photographs there.

Further visits followed on 8, 18 and 22 July, the first to fix up accommodation with the Symes at Green Ore for the summer holiday, the second a tour by car which included Gough's Cave at Cheddar, and the third a return to Burrington to locate Fox's Hole.

BURRINGTON 22 July 1911 (Saturday, with H. E. Harding)

Arrived at 2.40 p.m. Walked across fields to gorge and climbed up W. side opposite long stretch of horizontal strata and took panorama of this. From there we could see signs of Fox's Hole high up on the other side and a long way further up gorge. I had missed this on two previous occasions. I had located it this time through 6-in map, though this names it Aveline's Hole in error. It is three-quarters way up cliff opposite Ellick Wood just above S curve above E. Brooklet. It shows a bush of yew and some bare rocks from the road. After zigzagging up to it over loose surface scree we found it to be a vertical drop slightly inclining in to the cliff, av. 5–6 ft diameter all the way down, silted up at the bottom, resembles Plumley's Den but larger, 30 ft deep shown by reflected sunlight, shows promise of further galleries from one or two recesses now choked, a little work might clear these. Took three views at different points and scrambled down.

Balch had told me of Boyd Dawkins' hole on opposite side of W. Brooklet to Goatchurch. We looked for this and found a promising crack among loose boulders and in the nettles 15 ft above foot of path leading to Goatchurch, could see but a few feet in here and there, imperfectly examined by B.D., might get in by excavation. Took photo but it wants a distant one taken with morning light from other side of stream. We then took immediately below this the swallet at present acting for W. Brooklet. When this cannot take all, there are one or two subsidiary swallets further down W. Brooklet gorge. We took higher road to Morgan's and had tea. We were looking for Squire's Well and M [Morgan] reported this to be beyond lake at Rickford, but we could only find a dry trough which takes drainage of wood on W. of Blagdon Combe. Still to do swallets behind Mendip Lodge Wood and Squire's Well. Found no other signs of caves.

The summer holiday based at the Symes' cottage (Woodside) at Green Ore lasted from 23 August to 7 September, and it seems likely that Mortimer Savory stayed there with JHS for the whole period. The first ten days or so were spent at least partly in digging at Hillgrove Swallet, which was conveniently situated less than a mile S.W. of Green Ore. The swallet takes a sizeable feeder stream in wet weather and appeared to offer real prospects of something big underneath. However, despite a lot of hard work by JHS and his younger brother, results were consistently disappointing. (Spore-tests have shown that water entering this swallet reaches the Axe at Wookey Hole, together with water in other swallets including Swildon's Hole and Eastwater.) In view of their lack of progress, it is perhaps not surprising if the brothers' enthusiasm for the dig waned eventually. Whatever the reason, they spent little time at Hillgrove towards the end of the holiday, and in the last five days visited Lamb Lair Cavern, Sandpit Hole, Wookey Hole and Ebbor Gorge. On a walk with Balch at Ebbor on 3 September, JHS exposed the small rock shelter which came to be called 'Savory's Hole', in which he was photographed by Balch and to which he refers in the entry for 3 August 1921.

HILLGROVE 25 August 1911 (Friday)

Worked all the morning at a little fissure higher and to the right of B's [Balch's] proposed hole, though we did not know this at the time, filling in of leaves and earth had made levels different and accounts for mistake. After two hours' work of clearing earth and two boulders we came to a small vertical slit 1 in × 6 in, through which small stones dropped 2 or 3 ft. Removed one more boulder that morning and enlarged

Mr and Mrs Symes at their cottage door, Green Ore, where JHS often stayed; half-plate with flashlight (date unknown)

slit. After lunch made purchases in Wells for my birthday tea, after tea worked two hours and got out two more boulders, leaving one big one fixed in hole (which was now lower and larger) ready to come out on Saturday.

HILLGROVE 26 August 1911 (Saturday)

Worked morning and afternoon, got the one loose boulder out and cleared mouth a bit, got in and could drop, horizontal slit to left and rise beyond, water way to direct front but choked with silt. Balch came and said remove wedge boulders over entrance. This we did but it meant taking out two others and one stuck, we had to leave it over to Sunday. Tackle was used often.

27 August 1911 (Sunday)

Wells Cathedral for morning service. Took some measurements at Hillgrove of hole and swallets etc. in the afternoon.

HILLGROVE 28 August 1911 (Monday)

Morning and afternoon at hole, got wedge boulder out by flaking and started to trim the hole up making vertical sides. Could see one boulder just ready to fall from side, held him till I was clear then let him fall. He wedged badly so had to flake instead of tackle, after this was out there were three more on left to come out, on which we used tackle for last one.

HILLGROVE 29 August 1911 (Tuesday)

Took some photos, this last boulder weigh-

ed at least 6–7 cwt. After this we cleared sides again and started working underneath clearing earth out. Up to now had got out thirteen boulders altogether though some broken.

HILLGROVE 30 August 1911 (Wednesday)

Took hoe along this morning and found it very useful for pulling up the choke silt from passage way which was too narrow for comfortable work otherwise. Had bucket at the top and managed at a good rate, stopped at midday. Balch came and suggested getting more boulders out of the floor to make a good roomy cavity for a footing at mouth of hole. These were very tight having got there with huge pressure presumably. We got out two in the afternoon with great difficulty, remaining ones are wedged under edge of great lying boulder. We tried the propped boulder at mouth last thing and found it would give easily, got out of its way, knocked away props and it fell across mouth, bridging it.

HILLGROVE 31 August 1911 (Thursday)

Webb was to come up this morning. We broke up fallen boulder, very heavy, used tackle, took another out of side behind it also using tackle, also two from a new part of the floor which were badly wedged. Webb came and we worked some time at tightly packed choke in little channel now made in floor. We could at last get round shoulder of big lying boulder though very tight, could see a long straight passage, low and narrow, floor a narrow channel filled

22 February or April 1913. Gough's Cave: the best pagoda in Solomon's Temple; whole-plate

with choke matter, and right ahead a narrow flake had fallen from fissure in roof vertically and had stuck between roof and floor firmly with a small vertical slit on the left. We could not get anywhere near as far as this though.

LAMB LAIR 2 September 1911 (Saturday)

Took extensive photos at Red Quar and came back for Balch's letter. He had said to take ropes and pulleys to Hunters Lodge to meet him and Kentish in the motor. Left bikes there and went by car to Lamb Lair. We lashed 60 ft [rope] to stake, hole now being surrounded with fencing. Balch went down, lighting up about 15 ft down and after a long while we heard him yelling up from the bottom that there had been a dangerous fall of earth at foot of shaft, which still hung just ready to fall into the entrance to passage way, now a mere rabbit hole. Balch came up then Kentish went down to see, and myself after he came up, rather narrow on the way down, had to trust chiefly to ropes though ladder and timbers were safe in places. We all thought it wiser not to venture through it as it looked extremely doubtful. It showed how very much more dangerous it had been when Marle and Co. went down, leaving no one above even.

WOOKEY HOLE 4 September 1911 (Monday)

Had failed to find Sandpit Hole on two previous occasions but went out this morning to look for it, and when found I discovered it actually marked on 1-in Ordnance Survey. It is similar to Bishop's Lot swallet, smaller but sides more precipitous, rocks and scree showing and no trees. The attempted hole is on the S. side of it and goes in as per photo, under overhanging rocks but closes small with two keystones. They have blocked mouth with stones until further excavation. Took photos and also of Bishop's Lot on the way back. Should like to take kite photos of these two and also work at Sandpit Hole. Had an early tea and went down to Wookey Hole with Balch, McEwan and others and had a good long evening there. Did the upper caves on both sides, getting splendid photos of two stalagmite walls in the highest chamber on E. side and of Sentinel and new chamber on W. side. Pitch dark when we got out. Used Balch's new lamp for first time. Had taken quarter-plate and half-plate cameras.

3 September 1911. JHS at a rock shelter in upper Ebbor Gorge, later named Savory's Hole after him (see diary 3 August 1921); half-plate

EBBOR 5 September 1911 (Tuesday)

Had a good long morning at Ebbor with EMS [Mortimer], taking many photos from top down to tall scree and obtained some for reference of many small cave mouths, water holes and cracks, besides getting many good pictorial ones. Am still more enchanted with Ebbor, it seems so cut off from the world. There is such a huge amount to interest one. The narrow gorge half-way down is truly wonderful, there is a spring mid-way down this defile now protected by a stone slab. Had late lunch and slacked rest of the day.

WOOKEY HOLE 6 September 1911 (Wednesday)

Went down with Mortimer to Wookey Hole late in the morning and devoted a long afternoon to the three chambers, not going into E. or W. branches. It was at about 4.30 that we heard the noises in the first chamber described in detail in my report [this account also appeared in full in *Wookey Hole, Its Caves and Cave Dwellers*, by H. E. Balch, published 1914]. River was extremely low during all this period. One party only came in. We had the use of Balch's lamp, and took the Witch, big column, pools, mushroom and others, twelve views in all. On returning to Hillgrove House in the evening, we found the secretary on the lawn whom we had not met before. We had our overalls on and were very much daubed with mud, and he immediately sprang to the conclusion that we were airmen who had met with a mishap out in the grounds, and he offered us his very kind help. What next!

JHS and EMS packed up and returned home on Thursday 7 September after collecting some good samples of calamine at Miles Lot (in Green Ore wood) and photographing the old gruffs there. Later that month he went on a car drive with his mother and Bryan Savory, a tour that included the stone circles at Stanton Drew, Green Ore, Nordrach and Charterhouse. On the second Saturday in October, JHS went on another car drive to Mendip with his father and a friend, to Cheddar where they visited the show caves, had lunch at the Cliff Hotel and climbed Jacob's Ladder. They returned via Priddy and Hillgrove, to see the dig, and had tea with the Symes at Green Ore.

There then followed two caving expeditions when JHS was active with his camera, the first to Gough's Cave with one of the Gough brothers in late October, and the second to Wookey Hole with Balch and others in mid-November.

GOUGH'S CAVE 4th Saturday in October 1911

I went down alone to Cheddar by train early in the morning taking camera etc. and ropes; pouring rain. Gough met me at the station, drove up at once to cave and started without delay through the public parts of the cave. We took the same route as that described in *Netherworld of Mendip*, the following are the points that struck me. In the first chamber off the track the broken floor of stalagmite is very fine; it is a great question what caused this, varies from 2–4 in thick and is in millions of fragments. We procured a good photo

6 September 1911. Wookey Hole: looking over the pools between the first and second chambers; half-plate

showing this. There is a fine stalactite and curtain hanging alone side by side here of pure white, also some good small anemolites [erratic stalactites]. We then went through the dip and the next large chamber ('Babylon'), where there are huge fallen blocks. We also saw the small hanging floor in an offshoot chamber. We next arrived at the big drop and discussed for some time if it was wise to make fast a rope to the wedged boulder at top, this being a large pebble there appeared to be no grip to it. However, we decided to do so but leaving the camera behind. We arrived at the soak at the bottom and crawled through a short passage into the largest chamber. We looked up and saw far away the lighted taper we had left on the way on the top level; it seemed an immense distance up. What struck us on examination of the chamber by magnesium ribbon was a huge angular block of limestone of many tons, apparently fallen from the roof and just caught at one of its corners by a few inches against the arch of a second and lower chamber to the S., and thus prevented by this from falling into that chamber. It will be interesting to see whether this continued enormous pressure will at last make either the block or the arch give way. Another thing was a huge upright block with the appearance of being water-worn, standing on end at the top of a tall scree in a corner at the W. of the great chamber, and looking as if a mere touch would send it hurtling down to the floor of the chamber.

We slipped into the lower chamber, being very chary about going under the big boulder or disturbing anything near it, and here we found thick sand (instead of mainly scree as in the great chamber) with several old stream ways worn out. There were traces of digging here at the one on the left (E.?), but the very promising one to right had a perfectly smooth surface and one was able to push along some little way, the roof very gradually coming nearer although at one point there was a small rise and room enough to turn round. We retraced our steps to great chamber and pushed forward through devious ways into rocky passages just opposite the ones we had come out of. The roomy ways seemed to end as a cul-de-sac with the exception of one nearly upright ruckle of loose boulders. They would require careful manipulating but a climb would be interesting. We did not go up, but this would seem to lead to the higher levels

4th Saturday in October 1911. Gough's Cave: one of the Goughs in the chamber with the broken up stalagmite floor; half-plate

22 February or April 1913. Gough's Cave: the Opera Box and a fine stalactite wall to the left; whole-plate

again. Whether there are any connections from this end is difficult to tell. We examined many low small passages in the vicinity but none gave good promise and we did no digging. We shortly returned to the drop, climbed up without much difficulty and started homewards, taking various photos on the way including some on the public path. We had lunch in the Chamber of Babylon (the second large one from Niagara).

On reaching the entrance we at once proceeded to Gough's Old Cave. This is much smaller and apparently has no connection with the other. There are many weird shapes among the stalactites. We went up a winding stair and came to a lofty chamber with a huge cairn in it built by Gough senior, and on again upwards, and the way terminated with a small but fine grotto right back over our heads. This is not nearly as extensive as the new caves, about the size of Cox's in fact, and the whole looked very desolate through having been neglected so long. All the ironwork had rusted and much rubbish lay about. My photos represent the most interesting of the views to be found here.

WOOKEY HOLE 2nd Saturday in November 1911

Met Balch, Barnes and several others at the cross roads. We went up to the cave and proceeded to the third chamber. There were quite half-a-dozen cameras at work. The idea was to get a good photo of the last arch and after the prolonged dry season we have had this was deemed a suitable time for doing so. The water was exceedingly low and by holding lamps low we could see that there was a clear headway right through. The water was about 4 ft deep and one could have waded through, but shortly after entering the large chamber beyond there is a big drop in the river bed, probably indicating a lower channel for water. This makes it very difficult to photograph there except from a very stable raft, and this would not have passed through. It wants the lowering of the mill sluice here to help us pass through absolutely. I chose a position well to the left for the first flash. Balch stood up to the arch as near as possible and I got a fine result. For the second we had one or two figures in to give scale and my position was to front of entrance. This was underexposed. With

2nd Saturday in November 1911. Wookey Hole: Conglomerate Ceiling above the Boulder Bridge, east series; half-plate (This photograph was later coloured accurately, stone for stone, in shades of blue and red, see diary 28 September 1912.)

both we distributed the flashes so as to get no black shadows, but at the same time getting all the relief possible to show in the roof which is here very flat and a perfect arch. After picking up our traps we made our way to the eastern chambers, discussing the noises heard on the way. Our first halt in these chambers was under the fine flat Conglomerate Ceiling there exposed. I am anxious to take prints of this there another time and to initial the substance of each stone, limestone, sandstone etc., and so get an absolutely correct colour print of this to show its fine effect. We did not stop long but got a fine view and photo of one of the long passages higher and further south. By lighting it at intervals right along we showed its length splendidly. After this we did little more than have a look at the Spur and Wedge and the boulder floor before packing up and coming out.

The last expedition of 1911 was on Boxing Day to Coral Cave on the south side of Wavering Down, accompanied by Dick Savory. They went down the cave with Balch and Troup, and although JHS took photographs, these do not appear to have been successful because of the very wet conditions. However, on a subsequent trip down Coral Cave, probably in 1914 but which was not recorded for some reason, he obtained much better results.

CORAL CAVE, COMPTON BISHOP
26 December 1911

Dick and I started down by car at 8 a.m. with a big lot of kit comprising ropes,

pickets, bars, sledge, pulleys and camera kit, including some SMRE [South Midland Royal Engineers] stuff. We struck off the [Cross–Compton Bishop] road just after an S bend, and about 400 yd due up the hill from where a few houses come down to the road, in a corner of the rough common we found the hole protected casually by a little light brushwood thrown into the mouth. We set to work at once making an anchorage with a 5 ft picket and a 4 ft bar, we found a good crevice for the former giving good hold, about 10 or 12 ft due above hole. We retired to the shed where the ropes were keeping dry to await Balch and Troup, the first from Wells and second from Axbridge. We had waited about an hour when we heard voices and saw the two coming over the hill towards us. They had not come by the road all the way, so had missed the car and not brought the other stuff on from the village; accordingly Balch and I started back for Cross and fetched the other things, this took three-quarters of an hour and it was pelting all the time.

When we got back to the hole we first made fast the 100 ft 2¾-in rope to the anchorage and let it all down the hole, the 60 ft lighter (2½-in) rope we passed through a pulley made fast to anchorage, and brought so far forward as to overhang the brink of the hole. I had made a very good sling from a light 36 ft lashing, making a bowline on a bight with the rope attached to the free end. Balch harnessed up first and very cautiously dropped as far as the scree to see the lie of the land. Stones that slid forward and dropped over the edge seemed to fall into deep water. Again we three let out cauti-

Probably 1914. Coral Cave: Brownsey starting down the entrance vertical, with the safety line held by Barker and Perdue; half-plate

ously, especially as he neared the foot and at last he cried out to slacken away. He had found good standing room there with better in the grotto, though in all it was quite a confined space. The grotto forms a convenient shelter for those below, when people are following down on the scree up above. It is impossible to move on this latter without dislodging stones of various sizes. Balch went into the grotto and I followed down. It was very insecure on the scree and I had a rough time of it on the second half as, not knowing the lie of the land, I omitted to walk backwards down this bit but sat down and slid, with baggage on me too! However, I knew better for another time. We sent the sling up and they sent us down the camera, legs etc. The difficulty of getting the sling rope down over the shoulder was easily overcome by just giving it a half-hitch round the main rope and then those at the bottom holding it back clear of shoulder. It slid down then from top to bottom without a check. Of course if there is no main rope but only a sling, then nothing can be done but continuous casts from above till successful.

There was nothing for us to do but stand our ground and look round at what was to be seen. We examined the grotto first, and piling up some boulders showing good deposit, we photographed these *in situ*. Although this deposit is not nearly so fine as that in the Coral Cave itself, it was really very fine. On a shelf of rock immediately above, we found traces of the spiked antler variety (which reaches as many as ten branches – HEB) but for the most part it was of a round beaded form. Strangely enough the bed rock did not hold nearly so much as the small and large fragments which were on the floor and shelf mentioned. This latter would pay for examination as it may lead into the rock northwards (opposite way to Coral Cave). Balch, by standing on my back, could reach far enough to get good specimens but not enough to see right to the rear. A small ladder sent down would help. We got some specimens, putting them in a box of fine sand as they are so brittle. We then turned the camera across the chamber and got a bad photo, but showing enough to record the extremely high water level at this date, also a large vertical fault on opposite side. There were many insects down here, specially on the body of a dead sheep out in the water. The place is also made rather a rubbish hole by numerous tins, earthenware etc. thrown down. The first chamber is a rough oval and the arch over passage which dips and leads to Coral Cave was completely submerged. I took one more of Balch starting ascent to show its nature and then I started up, using a candle in my mouth this time. The lamp which I had had for Christmas proved very unwieldy going down and most troublesome. The first half going up is very straightforward, after giving the signal to haul from above you walk up the vertical rock, helping yourself with main rope which drops between your legs. The trouble begins when you get on the scree, you walk up as far as practicable so as to gain all possible height and then you signal again and with a hearty heave you are hanging in the air and spinning round too. Probably you make about 20 ft and then you near the bottle mouth, barking your shoulders and shins, it absolutely refuses a foothold till your

Probably 1914. Coral Cave: the second arch, with Brownsey in the entrance to a tributary passage above and Barker below; half-plate

shoulders are pretty well in the mouth, and then it is with difficulty that you find one, kicking about in the darkness below. I got out safely feeling more or less sore and then we let Troup down. Balch gave directions from below and it was not a long job. They sent the camera etc. up first and then Troup came up. Dick hauled near the mouth and I took a turn round my body and walked backwards down the hill, thus bringing them up at a good speed, all found it awkward getting out of the mouth; this was about 4 p.m. We packed up and the four of us struggled to Cross, very wet under a heavy load. The photos, by the way, had been taken under very trying circumstances, a deluge of large drops falling everywhere.

Probably 1914. Coral Cave: at the foot of the drop from the entrance, Brownsey (top), JHS and Perdue; half-plate

1912

In 1912 JHS continued to visit Mendip regularly and, as in 1911, spent his Easter and summer holidays there, staying at Green Ore again. Eleven out of a total of thirty-five diary entries for the year describe caving expeditions, and more than half of these were to Wookey Hole. Apart from a few cursory visits to see how much water was going down and the state of the dig, Hillgrove swallet received no real attention. Instead, Nedge Hill Hole, also near Green Ore, was the main target of digging activity in the summer holiday. At the end of the year, JHS became involved in producing the plates and many of the figures for an ambitious book based on the archaeological finds at Wookey Hole, to be written by Herbert Balch. The book, Wookey Hole, Its Caves and Cave Dwellers, was finally published in 1914 and was printed by Vandyck Printers, sister company of E. W. Savory Ltd. It had 300 subscribers, and JHS, as co-author (according to the contract), received one third of the royalties. As well as describing Wookey Hole and its environs, it also contains a chapter on Eastwater swallet, 'feeder to the River Axe', which emerges from Wookey Hole. Swildon's Hole, however, which was also thought (correctly) to be a feeder of the Axe, received no more than a few passing references. John Hassall, an artist friend of JHS, contributed some fine period restorations, based on archaeological finds, and line drawings to the book.

Another project that JHS started at the end of 1912 was copying and describing an ancient parchment map of Mendip, probably Elizabethan, which had originally been part of the Ashweek Court Rolls and had passed into the possession of Wells Museum. It concerned mining and commonage of the forest and hill of Mendip, and the copy, description and a summary of the laws and orders of the Mendip miners, commonly called Lord Choke's laws, were published in the WNHAS Proceedings for 1913. It was at about this time that JHS also joined the Somerset Archaeological and Natural History Society.

The first entries for 1912 were an evening photographic trip to Wookey Hole on 23 February, when JHS spent the night nearby at Adlam's, and a weekend stay at Green Ore on 23 and 24 March, when he went for walks in the vicinity with Mr Symes, notably to Hillgrove again and Nedge Hill to see the cave mouth there.

WOOKEY HOLE 23 February 1912

E. Gardiner, Wheeler, Barnes, Balch, JHS.

28 September 1912. Wookey Hole: the four and a half pillars, west series; half-plate

We five with young McEwan went up to the hole, donned our boiler suits at the entrance and first of all did the three main chambers. Water was much higher than last time. We had a look at the sand bank and also some interesting holes above it, leading I understand back to the E. boulder chambers. We also noted some good cave pearls 'in action' on the terraces of the second chamber. The current was extremely slow we noticed in the first chamber, because the sluice outside was down. We had left our traps at foot of W. series and coming back we picked them up and started through these. I took the climb this time (it is rather awkward) and fixed the rope ladder as usual. We left Balch and Wheeler at work at the inner end of the first tunnel where there was a depression in the sand giving good promise. We other four went on up, Barnes leading, and saw all the usual sights, going straight on to the Grill. I was the only one of the party that had been beyond before so I led the way. It was very moist and I did not find the difficulty I expected. There is a certain knack of getting through the last bit both as regards mode of progression and also position of body and arms. I pushed through and sitting in the mud held the light for Gardiner. He was getting into difficulties and suggested that he could not get through, even saying it was a little tight! But I persuaded him to stick to it and to alter the position of his body. He did this and got a few inches further, even near enough to grasp a knob of stalagmite with each hand, but even then he could not manage it, so reluctantly had to back out, McE and Barnes doing accordingly. Now McE had on fairly decent clothes and even now they did not look in good shape, so he decided to stay back with Gardiner, and Barnes came on again getting through after a bit of struggling.

We went at once to a large group of stalactites N. of the big bedding cave and got two good photos of this. Coming back we took an upright one of the rift looking N. with the stalactites in the distance. It shows the stalagmite walls very well and the tilt of the chamber above. We left the camera and went a little way in the opposite direction, but as time was getting on we started back. I came first and at the Grill turned about with the camera (which would just go through by the way) and took Barnes at the tight bit. We have since called this 'Purgatory', it came out well. We also stopped and took the '4½ pillars', a very striking feature of the chamber before the Grill. We noticed the excavation here and thought about analysing the sand; Barnes took some for this. We joined Wheeler and Balch who had done a surprising lot, having worked in 4 or 5 ft slightly downward into the soft wet sand, westwards. They stopped and we all journeyed forth.

HILLGROVE 23 March 1912

I left my bike at Green Ore and walked across the fields to Hillgrove. There was a strong brook running and every drop of it being consumed, and as regards the hole the boulders at the mouth seemed to be in rather a precarious state and will require testing. Some choke matter had got in but the new dam had caught the bulk, all the boulder work had been well washed out and one could now see daylight through to the far corner, which accounts for the cracks discovered previously (in the summer) on the interior. Water was coming through both of the holes we took to be rabbit holes and they were much enlarged. Behind the new dam it was filled up with silt and this water was nearly all soaking through here. I then went to a 'Trial Hole' just newly found which Balch had told me of by postcard and which Farmer Symes had put hurdles round. It is in the middle of the second field on the right going from Hillgrove to Priddy, a boy had been working the bar [probing] in this field and when over this spot it went clean through surface nearly leaving his hands. The spot was dug up and it collapsed together with a lot of masonry just below surface. The hole is now about 15 ft deep, very wet and liable to sink further I should say, sides are very insecure even now. These Trial holes or shafts are probably real workings, specially those with masonry, important shafts too, not trial as the country people call them (other name gruff, meaning groove). There are many others and it is not advisable to stand in the foot of any of the old surface 'crater' workings, as many may only be covered over the same as the above.

GREEN ORE 24 March 1912

In the morning first thing after breakfast Mr Symes and I set off for another walk, a strong sea breeze coming over us. We went up Furzewell Hill past Rookery Farm where I saw a good size swallet although it was dry. I have marked it on map, its valley seemed as big as that of Red Quar, stream runs into it southward. We continued up the hill to Island Cover which was most interesting. At its lower (S.) end is a fine little swallet, as large as the one above mentioned and a small stream running briskly to earth through the undergrowth and moss covered stones. Its entrance is quite loose and open stonework, and it seems to be much in use.

Soon after lunch Balch and Barnes arrived on bikes and we went at once with Mr Symes to the extreme top of Nedge Hill where Wicks a few weeks previously had discovered an extremely promising cave mouth. We saw on the way, at the end of the drove leading out onto Wells road, a huge pile of loose limestone and the remains of a kiln. Trees were growing in the midst which prove it to be twenty years old or more. These had not been hauled up there on purpose we thought, but are probably old walls pulled down to enlarge fields in days gone by and burnt on the spot to save hauling. We took a line up towards the E. shoulder of the hill and there met a surprise. It really seemed a ready made cave for us. A huge flat open mouth (at the foot of a little valley) facing S., quite a steep slope of large scree leading down into it. There were two or three depressions to its immediate N. but the largest and the deepest was to the S., none of them apparently taking drainage. It was discovered while hunting and is blocked up to prevent foxes going to earth. I will take photos of it at first opportunity in its natural state before anything is disturbed. It is on Lord Waldegrave's estate. Dip of strata here is 45° to S. The place was rich with small ferns and a certain wet brown spongy vegetable matter was clinging to the rocks everywhere. A fine bed of cave sand was on the left and it is near here the most promising spot for excavation. We examined a rough enclosure at foot of hill S. of this, surrounded with fine beeches, which proved to be an old lime working.

JHS's Easter holiday lasted a week from Thursday 4 April until the following Wednesday, and he spent four of those days underground. Owing to a rail strike, he had to cycle from Bristol on the 4th, but his parents took his kit ('photographic and otherwise together with 30 ft, 60 ft, 100 ft 2¾-in and two 50 ft ropes and two blocks. This was in case, for Eastwater on Monday') out to Green Ore by car on their way further south. He met Balch in Wells, who had arranged Ebbor for the next day, and also Barnes who had arranged any day for Swildon's with Hipsley the agent.

EBBOR GORGE 5 April 1912 (Good Friday)

I cycled to Wookey Hole via the crossroads, meeting Wheeler walking on the Wells to Wookey road. Balch soon overtook us on his bike and we left our bikes at Adlam's after getting some provender in the village. We walked N. of [Tower] rock a little way and soon came to the Outlook Cave, a small place where already much work had been done. We spent an hour or more clearing the entrance passage and immediately beyond this, the others building a good platform with the debris which we threw out, to prevent it rolling to the bottom. We

cleared a lot first at entrance end of first chamber and later at further end, but in the mean time Wheeler and I slipped down into the second chamber. It slopes with the ground outside and at its lower end are signs of rabbit holes and loose stones indicating communication with the open air. All round the rest, the floor gradually meets ceiling and ends with stalagmite spattered pebbles and stones mostly sealed to the ground, and making progress at any point is very hard. We were able to clear 2 ft on W. side to left of entrance (looking in) and then came to a full stop. It was the same all the way round. In turning over the cave sand about here we made a few interesting finds, namely boar's tusk, bear's foot bone and human teeth and ribs. We worked until sure that we could make no headway and then came out and resumed work in first chamber, leaving off about 4 p.m. A point in the second chamber evidently did at one time communicate with the inner passages but now we think a point in the first chamber is the best to work at, one sees down a rabbit hole here into the clear below some fissures. There is easy head room to work here and everything is not sealed down as in the second chamber. Two very fine greater horseshoe bats were in the second chamber and in the fissure of first chamber which goes nowhere. It was settled next time to work at the point in the first chamber.

SWILDON'S HOLE 6 April 1912 (Saturday)

We arranged yesterday for a small party to visit here but it ended in only Barnes senior [Ernest Barnes' father], HEB and myself

5 April 1912. Outlook Cave, Ebbor Gorge: Balch and Wheeler digging in the first small chamber; half-plate

putting in an appearance. On arrival, although the weather had been exceptionally dry for some time, we found a strong stream flowing. The little swallow to right was taking a good bit of water, more than on other occasions because of our work at it, but not even now nearly enough. When the plug was put in (after much difficulty on account of accumulated weed) the water hesitated for a little while the small hole worked to full advantage, but this being overwhelmed soon, the water made fast headway for the top of the dam, taking perhaps three-quarters of an hour to fill up. Notwithstanding the fact that the small hole was working well, even now the amount of water going through the hole made it just impossible to descend. We held a council of war as to what was best to be done and finally we decided to see what could further be done to the small swallow. We emptied the dam and guided as much water as possible down the main stream in order to keep former dry. But before we had finished it was quite plain that an important thing to do (now that a dammed pond is not needed) is to thoroughly excavate this hole during dry weather, so that it will always take enough water to allow of getting in at any time. We worked in turn at the hole solidly up to lunch time, constantly putting in the sluice plug to see how much water it would take. We were much delayed at first by continuous falling in of the mud round the roots of the hawthorn and finally by quite a big fall. I spent ages upside down with my head in this hole and my knees on hardly uncovered stones in the streamlet and my hands in icy cold water. The result

was a splitting head. There was some little stream all the time and every now and then something was removed that let a huge lot of water down with a rushing gurgle and then something would fall to stop it all again. But in the end it was rather better than at first, though not sufficient and the dam filled up in perhaps half as long again.

We had lunch, debating the while what to do. At last we settled that it was safe enough to do as follows. We first got hold of a responsible looking farm hand and gave him explicit instructions to pull up the sluice plug at 3 p.m. and 5.30 p.m., empty dam and replace. We did not anticipate a long stay underground as our party was small and as so much time was wasted in the morning.

Plan and section of Swildon's Hole, surveyed by the MNRC (mainly R.D.R. Troup) and drawn by JHS for its 1921 Annual Report

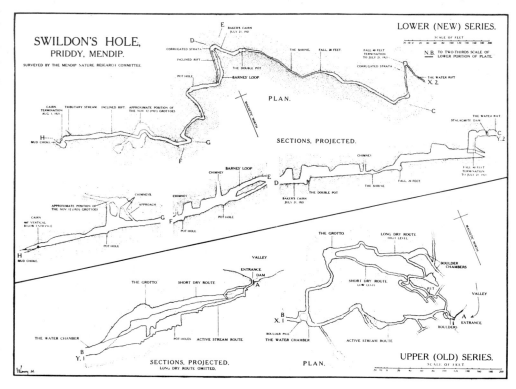

We started in at 2.40 with kit reduced to a minimum for speed. Going down the new cut, we unpacked all photographic kit and perched ourselves on the ledge of the return into the first water chamber, with camera enveloped in a mac and focussing cloth and powder and pan carefully covered up until the right moment. Balch was on the ledge right along facing the chamber, I was as far forward as I dared go and Barnes was behind me. It was now nearly 3 p.m. and we waited anxiously for any new sound. At last it came, in the distance we heard a dull vibrating roar approaching which came louder and louder until it thundered with a rush into the first water chamber, seeming altogether to envelope the stream already running there. At first our breath was quite taken away and although we knew we had only a few minutes of it, we could not help but stare. It was not just the increase of the one stream, but fresh streams broke in from everywhere practically, and a most unexpected and inconsiderate one started just behind Balch's head, making him do a dash for safety. He took his stand on my left and uncovered the flash pan and set off the touch. It seemed ages going off and in the hurry a candle was flashed across the lens. The flash went off but of course it was then no good so I hurriedly changed the plate, set another flash for Balch again, and squatted in the same place with the camera between my knees hoping for the best (a stand was impossible in the angle and in such a hurry). Again wiping the lens we had another shot, the water had not abated and this time all went well, although I could see the flash had gone partly in the lens. The difficulty was

that we were three-quarters to the roof of the chamber and outside it and round a corner. Of course it was impossible to get anywhere inside for the job, and the only thing we got [in the photograph] was the first fall or line of water drops which usually one dodges under to enter chamber, together with just a shadow of the water rushing away behind. It was quite crooked but it was wonderful to get anything at all under the circumstances. This is the first time that the chamber has been seen in these conditions.

The waters now began to abate and soon it was normal, although we found it far too wet to use rift comfortably. However, as we had no photo at all of the chamber we went down and I squatted on a streaming

6 April 1912. Swildon's Hole: the upper water chamber in the active stream route. The sluice was opened above and this photograph was taken after the first rush of water was past; half-plate

boulder with my half-plate camera covered up in front of me. My feet extended into the stream with the camera case on my insteps and the flash on top of that. After many efforts in the damp atmosphere I got touch paper going and waited an age for the flash, in the meantime I found the mac was smouldering and burning my hands badly. I knocked it out, shaking the camera and everything seemed to go wrong, but the flash went off in the end and I got an excellent photo. While climbing up again, I slipped and cut my hand open badly in catching the sharp waterworn rocks, though only slipping a foot. I felt pretty miserable now, what with cut and burnt hands. I tied up with a handkerchief and we went on a little way down the waterway, prospecting for further views but they were difficult and not interesting, and I felt very disinclined for hanging about there with my hand streaming with blood. So we packed up and came up the new cut to the old S bend. While the other two worked at a stinking mass of green stuff and stones there, I went up to the mouth to see how the dam was, which was now filling and also to fix up my hand. Head was pretty bad at the time, but we decided to go on even though time was short. Everywhere it was rather wetter than the last visit, though we had had much dry weather. I joined the others again and, passing on kit, we got under way, and after passing the rough bits of the S bend and inclined rift we soon reached the beginning of the stalactites. We made our way slowly down to the stalactite grotto by the long dry way, the muddy bits seemed worse than usual, extremely soft and deep. We showed Barnes all the best places and, on reaching the grotto, started to photograph the lowest corner from the stalagmite bridge, Balch going underneath after the first flash and illuminating the furthest parts. It turned out excellently. We also took an upright one of what is in future to be called the 'Pagoda' as a landmark. One of the first things I noticed there was the little strap from my canteen sack which I lost last time, and which was lying in a pool.

Time was now getting on so we hurried on down, taking the giant stoup on the way. As we approached the lowest chamber we heard a tremendous roar, and found that we were lucky enough to be on the spot in time to see the result of the sluice being opened for the second time. It was deafening and away in the gloom we could see the extra rush of water. Of course, compared with many things, it was not colossal, but the interesting fact was that, just as in the first water chamber, it had not been seen under flood conditions of any sort before, no way up to now having been devised for safe travelling with anything like a lot of water going. We clambered onto the island, camera and all. I remembered the spot where Balch had his ducking, but by the time we had got as far as the falls, the water had reached normal again and, being short handed, there was nothing worth the taking, especially as the one done there before by quarter-plate, with a large party, was quite satisfactory. We were keeping our eyes on the time now and turned our steps upwards, stopping to photograph the tall flow of stalactite just above the lowest chamber and also the terraces, although this latter did not

37

6 April 1912. Swildon's Hole: Balch at the lower end of the Old Grotto; half-plate

come out owing to the hurry. On reaching the grotto too we wanted to try and take the fine assortment of stalactites behind the hanging column, but thought it inadvisable to waste further time as the dam above had been filling for some time now, so we hurriedly packed up and made for the surface. We did not stick at anything and, being a small party, must have made it in record time, say half to three-quarters of an hour, although we slightly overshot the point of ascent at the steep inclined rift, a thing easily done. The boulders round the S bend too were very tight to squeeze through and this is a piece of the passage to have well in mind, it was heavy work but we soon reached daylight. I was leading all the way up and on pushing my head out of the entrance, found a small crowd of curious farm hands awaiting us there. The one had carried out our instructions minutely about the water and we found there was still another 1½–2 ft to go when we reached the top, which would probably have taken another 40 minutes. But still, it would be extremely unwise to allow the slightest risk in this respect and it is also most important to leave matters in responsible hands before going down. If caught in the S bend or anywhere close to it on either side, things could be quite uncomfortable. We walked back to the farm looking very picturesque and there soon packed up and got under way for Hunters Lodge, where we had a fine warming tea.

The following day was Easter Sunday. JHS went to early service at the Green Ore Mission, and then after breakfast went for another walk with Mr Symes along past Red Quar to Miners Arms. After investigating various barrows and large depressions, they returned to Green Ore for lunch and in the afternoon JHS 'stayed near home'.

EASTWATER 8 April 1912 (Easter Monday)

My first caving exploit, with the exception of twice at Wookey Hole, was here in June 1910, and since then the mouth has been further improved in the stonework and lately an iron grating fixed over it. Balch had fixed up a party on Saturday and at about 9.15 a.m. Wheeler arrived on his bike with his traps and Holly on a motor bike. The others [Balch, Barnes and Webb] were

Projected section of Eastwater Cavern, by H.E. Balch, 1913

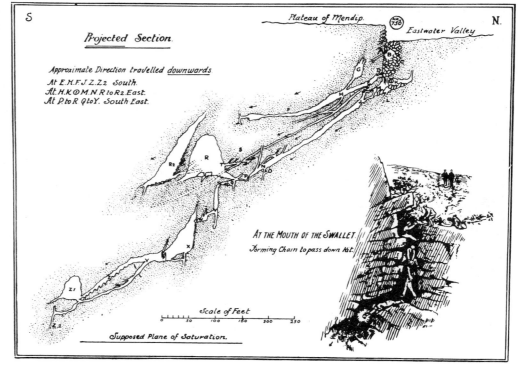

8 April 1912. Eastwater: Webb in the passage where one leaves the boulders for bedrock, at the entrance to the Boulder Chamber; half-plate

going straight to Eastwater from Wells. We each took a share of the ropes, canteen, camera and all the other things and got under way. We did not anticipate a very serious day, but there were some new passages (or rather crevices) showing in the Boulder Chamber which we were anxious to try with the ropes. Amid much good humour we made our way to the cave mouth, picking up those things which had been left at the gate on the way up to the farm. Wheeler led the way, this was at 11 a.m., and Barnes, Holly and Webb went down immediately after him. They took all the kit except the camera and haversack, and for a long time we heard their groans going downward towards the Boulder Chamber. Balch and I made a halt at the foot of the first (entrance) drop and got a splendid photo of him standing in the trap door, a flat boulder which if it fell would effactually close the whole place. We then went about half-way through the ruckle and took another very typical boulder photo showing well the character of the rocks, with Balch climbing over a flat inclined boulder. Then we went down to the head of the 380 ft Way (we could hear the others in the Boulder Chamber) to Bomb Corner as I propose calling it, and took one of Balch actually standing half in the pipe leading vertically down to the Boulder Chamber. It is just large enough for the body and very awkward to get a purchase with the hands. It was here that the solid column of water stopped the party from getting out for some time back in August ? [28.8.10], a description of which appears in *Blackwoods* [magazine]. The bomb did not move much,

only splitting one big vertical boulder, and there are still three or four in quite a precarious position which are to be very much avoided. (On trying to scramble up the pipe afterwards I started one sliding a little. It was only a small one but if it had slid towards me might have pinched me into the hole. Balch yelled down from ahead to know what on earth it was. However, it only went a little way down towards the 380 ft Way.)

After taking the photo at the pipe we joined the others in the Boulder Chamber. The wedged boulder at its mouth is another bad bit, some small stones not as big as your fist alone holding it up in a vertical position.

The Traverse in Eastwater, showing the method of reaching the 380 ft Way from the Boulder Chamber. Pen drawing by H.E. Balch, 1913–14

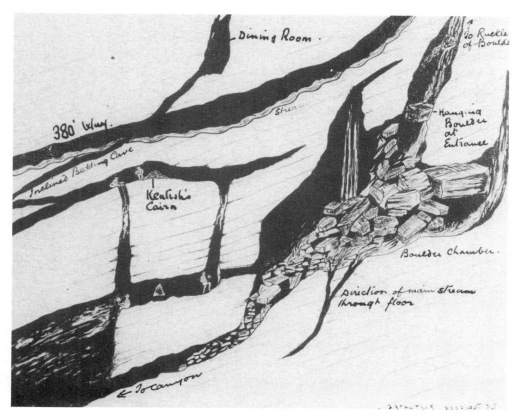

There is a question whether this big fellow ought to be sent going, but there is no knowing how much of the suspended scree and boulders in the chamber might not be started by it, and it also might plunge straight down into the exit in a straight line below it and block that. We were going to take a photo here and also have lunch, it being on the way for 12.30 p.m. So while some of the party travelled a little way down the Canyon in quest of water, we made preparations for the photo, taking up a position on the sand at the lowest point in the chamber, as close to the wall as possible and looking up towards the entrance past all the loose boulders with the party sitting on them. I made a slight mistake by locally lighting the foreground with wire after the flash had gone off, and this showed up the fumes, but the result is quite passable. We all noticed how remarkably dry it was for Eastwater, if ever a place is wet this is it, and notwithstanding that it had been raining outside, the drops were quite few and it was even difficult to find water for soup. We heard the efforts of the water party on their return journey, and soon the canteen, after many adventures, was handed into the chamber three parts full of water. We all opened fire on the lunch and soon the soup was going round too, just fine it was, I am to have cook's certificate. Wheeler had tried the two holes on one of the ropes but nothing came of either, he got as far as 50 ft into one but not into the other at all. We then packed up everything and, leaving ropes and canteen behind, we proceeded down the Canyon with camera and haversacks.

Immediately out of the Boulder Chamber, Balch pointed out to me the chimney proper overhead and the cleft in an opening immediately to left, both of which lead up to quite near Kentish's Cairn in the Traverse. This is one end of the Traverse in fact, which, together with the complicated passageway connecting it to the Canyon, form two of the most important keys of the whole cave system, as was proved when a party took the officers down from Priddy and was stopped by the water as mentioned before. We went on down the upper Canyon, not stopping on the rough part until it takes a turn to the left, and here we snapped four of them in the lower Canyon, one beyond the other. This [photograph] shows well the shape of pipe that the water has cut and is also the best of it taken so far. This pipe is really in two sections and at the end of the second comes the S bend, which was more or less dry and not nearly so tight as I was led to expect. I saw the peculiar leaf stalac-

Diagrammatic section showing assumed drainage of water from Eastwater swallet to Wookey Hole exit, by JHS, 1913

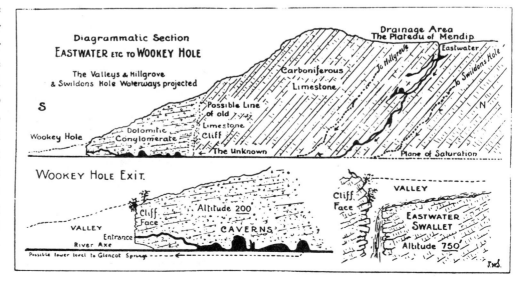

tite or anemolite in a small water passage up to the left. This gives one the idea that it has shelled off in part from the rock above through water action of some sort, and been left joined only at one side. Immediately after this the rift begins, and an early section has to be done with back and foot at 10 or 12 ft from the gully below. After this you have to travel along in the gully itself for some time, with the great rift above you going on up and up into darkness where no light has ever yet been made to penetrate. Just about here, near a bend to the left and up a small cavity to the left, you see a group of practically the only stalactites in Eastwater. Then you go on where the rift closes down a bit, getting narrow and forcing you to crawl. After going under a low arch, rather tight, you come into the second great rift chamber; it is also extremely high and you enter it on the floor nearly at its lower end with a steeply ascending scree running up it to the left. It is so steep that it is almost on the move and indeed the two Balchs had a bad time of it the first time the chamber was entered, as they started a great avalanche of the scree which rolled to the foot, quite blocking the small hole by which they had entered. They spent a long time trying experiments and moving away the rubble at different points to find the exit. It is possible, though dangerous through falling stones, to climb a considerable way up at its higher end from where the scree merges into the rock itself, wedging yourself up in the angle on the way. Balch went up some way on a previous occasion like this, but many stones were dislodged on the men below. I took a photo here which gives the appearance of height very well, it shows Balch looking into the dead blackness above.

We now thought about returning so faced about and started the journey up and up. Near the S bend I went off to the right with Barnes and Holly round a double angle and saw the head of the first vertical. It looked very imposing, a yawning black gulf, and stones thrown down clattered on and on it seemed endlessly down the inclined rift. There is a splendid upright pillar to lash ropes and pulleys to while manoeuvring this and also a similar one I am told for the second vertical. We joined the party and did not have a serious stop again before the Boulder Chamber, except for a photo in the upper or rocky Canyon looking up, and

8 April 1912. Eastwater: on the steeply sloping dangerous floor of the Boulder Chamber, Webb, Wheeler, Balch, Holly and Barnes; half-plate

another to show the back and foot work. On both occasions Wheeler waxed very humorous. On the first he being laid out like a corpse in a tomb, on a ledge of rock in the side out of the way and being made the butt of much chaff to which he was hardly in a position to reply in kind, and over the rift he found suddenly half-way through the exposure that the exact spot he had chosen to sit on was the point at which a small streamlet from the roof *would* run down his neck. He hurriedly did a bunk amid yells of laughter as I clapped the cap on, with vows to have it out with us when we were all out. We soon all found ourselves back in the Boulder Chamber, where we made a short halt while I got a fairly good snap of the big wedged boulder in upper exit, which it is prohibited to touch, by lighting from behind and this was thrown up pretty well. Then, while the others were clearing out, I tried to get one of Wheeler in the lower exit but this was not so successful. Then we followed them, I brought up the rear up to half-way through the ruckle and got a nasty turn at top of the pipe where, when trying to get a purchase with my elbows at its mouth, I started one of the smaller detached boulders sliding as mentioned before. We had gathered up all our kit and were making the best of our way to the mouth now. Wheeler and Webb brought up the rear and Balch and Barnes were the first to get out. The ruckle is a thing I must thoroughly master at an early date as very few know well the way through the boulders. The new tenant farmer [Loxton] and his son were at the top to meet us and we took a final photo before going up to the farm for our bikes.

WOOKEY HOLE 9 April 1912

Cycled down from Green Ore to HEB's for further cave negs and went on with him to Wookey Hole at 11 a.m. The mill hands were all idle on account of the coal strike so five of them came up to assist. Sheldon and Chiswell came up and chatted for some time while we carried on with the systematic digging just to the right, inside entrance. We had a good day's finds including a good red deer antler pick, *sawn* off at stout end (marks of saw), three new patterns on rough earthenware fragments, mother-of-pearl fragments, a good piece of bear's lower jaw, and a most perfect roebuck antler which was dug out of some black clayey fire ash of an

8 April 1912. Eastwater: Holly and Wheeler with nothing much below them in the passage below the Canyon; half-plate

old hearth, and which Balch informs me smelt abominably when he got it home. We did not come across this time any hearth stone lias such as was taken in from Wattles Hill opposite. Our method was to dig and break up buckets full of the unturned earth and put it on a large board under a good light on a ledge, and turn over every atom with a flat stick, gradually pushing it all off the board and throwing it back finally onto a finished patch. We went right down to bed-rock everywhere, even removing or breaking up many a tough boulder to get at the cave earth underneath. A tall piled up scree just inside entrance was very profitable and it is generally found that all the best things are obtained near the walls of the particular chamber in question or under overhanging ledges. The reason is obvious, namely that in the days that they came there, things were pushed aside or thrown into corners or gradually worked there where they were not disturbed, and in consequence were not trodden underfoot or broken up like they would have been if left out in the centre of the floor. The scree near door mentioned above had to a great part collapsed the previous day onto a spot where a few minutes before a small boy had been sitting watching the work; it was a near thing. They have put in many good days just lately in order to take full advantage of the mill hands' help. We knocked off work at about 3 p.m. and I went to Adlam's and had a good lunch while the others dispersed in different directions.

On 10 April, the last day of the holiday, JHS walked through Miles Lot to Rookery farm, *then to Island plantation and Nedge Hill Hole where he took photographs of the cave mouth. In the afternoon he walked to Nedge Wood and then Hillgrove to see the swallet, before setting off on his bike to catch the evening train from Wells to Bristol, Mr Symes having already taken his kit to the station in the morning.*

The next entry is for 22 April, when JHS and his artist friend John Hassall went on a drive out to Burrington, Charterhouse, Cheddar, Ebbor, Hillgrove and Green Ore, returning via the stone circles at Stanton Drew.

MENDIP 22 April 1912

I rigged John Hassall up in my togs, and we

8 April 1912. Eastwater: at the entrance after coming out; left to right, (above) the farmer, Holly, Barnes, Wheeler and JHS, (below) the farmer's son and Webb; half-plate

started in the car about 9.30 a.m. with Frances and Bryan [Savory], going over the bridge and down to Brockley Combe in the usual way. Everything was in full leaf and bright sunshine everywhere, a little quarrying still goes on near the top of the combe. We turned to the right on the Bridgwater road, branching off and over the level crossing to Burrington. We did not go on the hills at all but JH and I got out and just had a look at Plumley's Den and went down Aveline's Hole till just out of sight of daylight, where there is a mud choke round a slight bend to the right. There was much clay everywhere down the sloping passage of say 70 ft. We put up a few bats and examined one or two pipes overhead near entrance which proved to be nothing. We walked up the gorge to the car which had stopped just under Fox's Hole and this I pointed out to JH. We then made our way to Cheddar via Wright's Piece. We all got out at the top of Cheddar Gorge proper and JH and I clambered about on the W. slope getting some views with the Goerz Anschutz camera from levels about half-way up, these were improved by this and rather good. When we reached the little railed in tank I spotted for the first time the Long Hole and we went some way into this with matches only, 20 ft and came across a rotten pig at the top of what seemed to be a long greasy slope down, so we did not venture further not having any kit with us, this must be done soon. Went on down to Gough's and did the caves there, I had permission to show Hassall the Chamber of the Broken Floor. We did this, looked at the small anemolites and I also picked up my old flash pan which had

been there since I photographed there. We examined the small drop among the boulders to the further connections and I found I was not certain of the direction of the exit to these, but we did not intend to go further so walked back to the entrance by ourselves with lamp and candles.

We then all had grub, I took the two water exits here and we started off along the S. slopes of the hills on the way to Wells. We branched off to the left along a road which took us over the railway line into the W. end of Wookey Hole village. Here JH and I got out with bags, tools etc. We made our way through the hamlet of Ebbor and up the gorge, striking round the back of Tower Rock which is the easiest way up. I soon saw down through the trees our wall of excavated earth and we did not lose much time before we were at work down inside, having stowed our coats inside the entrance. It was highly amusing, I got in some little way in front of JH and had time to slip down through the small hole into the lower chamber, so that by the time he was onto the floor of the first I had entirely vanished as far as he was concerned and this puzzled him. He got a start when he heard a voice from apparently under his very feet, he was right over the hole. We dug for an hour and found nothing though we had moved a considerable amount of earth from where the passage ought to be. As time was getting on we hurried out and went up the gorge, through the ravine, looking at all the holes on the way, Balch's spring here was running strong. We broke out of the gorge to right just at the fence and made our way past the old iron workings as shortly as possible into

22 February or April 1913. Gough's Cave: Niagara Falls; whole-plate

Dursdon Drove at the end of which we saw the car which had waited some time for us.

On 5 June, JHS wrote that he was 'In town at Whitsuntide so could do nothing then'; also 'Have bought the half-plate from Biggs, it has done splendid work. HEB says he has seen nothing to beat it on account of accuracy of focus and small compass and wide angle.' There is no indication of what make 'it' was.

E. A. Baker had invited JHS 'for the Irish trip in August and I accepted but later had to cancel because of short holidays on account of my stay in town.' Instead he stayed at Green Ore, this time with Dick Savory, for two weeks from 20 August until 2 September. On the first day they went by train to Wells in pouring rain, taking their bikes and 4½ cwt of luggage. Mr Symes met them with his cart and took the luggage while they shopped and JHS bought four numbers of Archaeologia for 2/- in Wells Cathedral. In the afternoon they walked in oilskins to Rookham to see Balch at his bungalow, and he told them of the new slit just below the ravine in Ebbor Gorge where digging had just started and good things had been found, including a complete skeleton of a young child and a fine barbed flint arrowhead.

During a break in the storm they walked to the other (Baker's?) bungalow and then up to the 'point' to have a look round. 'The storm cloud effects were really beyond description. From here can be seen Brent Knoll, Bristol Channel, Poldens, Quantocks and Exmoor, two of the tors on Dartmoor, Camelot, Glastonbury Tor and flats, the Golden Cap, Westbury white horse on Shaftesbury Hill and many other places too numerous to mention. Just below us was Vigo Wood which with another wood eastwards on same level is always steaming when there is going to be wet weather. Nobody has been able to give any reason for this, why should these two only steam? "When Vigo smokes the rain will continue", this is the local saying.' After returning to Green Ore for a late tea, they were able to cycle in the dry to Red Quar, where a good stream was flowing down. 'Had supper and turned in early after testing the two cameras. We have not got the G.A. [Goerz Anschutz] this year.'

21 August 1912

First thing after breakfast we took the small pick and shovel and went up to Nedge Hill Hole. Much water was dropping but it was just the same as last time. We spent a short time at the likely spot on the right, which at first sight looked promising and we could see in 3 ft. Just as we were about to leave, however, I happened to see a good spot on the left, and on turning out earth and stones which had evidently been packed in to stop foxes, we could see in to a very promising low small round chamber. Two saddlebacks are in the floor just at entrance and these must be moved. Also roof is split and loose here and needs propping, a big lump fell on my hand while excavating the stones. However, for such a short time this gives us very good hopes of getting at something good.

Then we came home and got our cameras and biked to Priddy where the autumnal fair was on. It was quite interesting to see this deserted village so full of life. There were

21 August 1916. Priddy Fair, view of the Green looking towards the Batch; half-plate

very few cattle owing to the foot-and-mouth, but plenty of horses and sheep. We got some good photos. We called at Eastwater on the way back; there was a good stream going though not overflowing the dam. We got views of the entrance and stream, and immediately after got caught in a heavy storm. We rushed home, got a hurried lunch, changed, took half-plate, stand and bag and set off through driving rain for Wookey Hole. We went straight up to the cave and soon Balch joined us there, Webb and Barnes following from Ebbor soon after. There was a huge torrent of water going over the dam. Polypody was growing well on elm and elder (HEB says he had not seen it on elder before). Balch pointed out that with all the rain we had had, the line of dropping water was not nearly so far in towards door as is sometimes the case after an occasional storm; one can never account for the vagaries of water.

The bumping noises had been heard just previously by McEwan the guide. They were rather slower than when EMS [Mortimer Savory] and I heard them, but same style, and this was the first time in all his experience that he had heard them, having been in the cave hundreds of times. Also, they were located at entrance of third chamber this time, entrance to which was barred by flood. He was standing near the end of the bridge and roughly timed them at one every two or three seconds. River in the cave was very high, and it was inches over the bridge going into the third chamber so we could not enter. This we took and then went back into the first chamber. We got a very fine effect on the river end of it by illuminating from the big hole in the rock overlooking the river (the Aperture). Afterwards we all got up there, the first time for me, and it was simply fine to look down through this large hole onto the river and Witch lighted down below. We took a photo of Barnes, Webb and RNS in the bedding cave leading to the opening; it is an easy climb up. Here Webb and Balch had to leave us so Barnes and ourselves went on through the old ways as they are called, through a long rift and by branch passages till ultimately we came out in the top chamber near the surface of the cliff where the two streams of stalagmite are. There is a very fine 'oxbow' in one place and we photographed a parting of the ways where a large and very narrow flake of rock divides the two. We missed the right passage and found ourselves in a cul-de-sac. On turning round I, who was then leading, was very startled to find no way out. It was just concealed by a leaf of rock and all I could see was a small fissure high up through which I was sure we had not come. We soon found the right passage and after a low bend and a twist, emerged to my surprise into the big top chamber of the two streams of stalagmite (the Crow's Nest). At the opposite end was a glint of daylight and a huge crow's nest, while under our feet we could hear the roar of the river, with every now and then at irregular intervals a distant and faint boom, say six times. What was this? Very improbably blasting at Arthur's Seat; this was suggested at the time. We faced about and were soon in the passage with a fissure at the side which I had taken during a night's work from Bristol. Another drop and we were at the Conglomerate Ceiling, and yet another just beyond it and we were on the Suspended Boulders. These I took with RNS on them from the Wedge, showing the space above them and below. We dropped again and came round the corner on a level with the foot of Spur and Wedge. I went along to the end of the rift and, by using the legs as a platform, pushed the camera over to the far side, thus getting the whole of the Spur and Wedge and the space among the boulders to the passage side of them. Then we packed up and got out as quickly as possible. I fetched my lamp, which would not burn, from the first chamber; we saw no bats. It had stopped raining when we got out after four and a half hours at 7.30.

22 August was a 'slack' day when JHS and RNS visited Hillgrove swallet in the morning to inspect the dig and see how much water was going down ('a goodish stream'), and walked to the top of Pen Hill in the afternoon.

NEDGE HILL HOLE 23 August 1912

Weather still very bad. Arrived at Nedge Hole at 10.30 and started work at the likely spot on the left. All the work we did seemed to be through stones and sand that had been packed in some years ago. We turned out two fragments of pot a good many years old, also some fine stalagmite shell which had formed in a crevice and then dropped out. We worked until 12.30 and by this time there was just enough room to crawl through an arch which was gradually widening as we got down lower into the small chamber before mentioned. It looked extremely promising. I could see a large saddleback at the very end, over which stones I threw dropped a few feet. There were traces now of short stalactites and wavy frills. I did not get right in as the further end of our passage was still tight and the chamber small. There was still a considerable amount of earth and stones to come out. We came home to lunch and waited for R. Balch and Webb who we expected at 2.30. They did not come till 4 p.m. as they had had to finish up at Ebbor so we just went up for me to show them the hole which they had not seen. We did not intend to do any work. They were delighted with the cave and both thought our passage quite promising. R. Balch who is small went right in. The whole place was much more solid than I had imagined and they had no fear for the entrance. He got right up to the saddleback and on the other side found an inclined depression with a small tunnel choked at its mouth but roomy beyond, leading straight forward out of the lower end. We think this is the continuation of the water way. We ought to have a geologist's opinion as to age and nature of this cave. What surprised us was that the whole floor of the inner chamber seemed to be a false one or suspended. However, it might only be the way in which the packing had been thrown in. RB moved the saddleback easily, but in pushing it in front of him towards the entrance it sank several times right in the soft floor between the stones. We decided it was best to leave it until we had room to tackle it and the floor from the passage side. One other point was a small round worn

22 February or April 1913. Gough's Cave: reflected stalagmite pillars of pure white and red at top of the steps; whole-plate

water hole just inside to left which rose and then dipped beyond. Stones thrown in fell a little then struck water. All round this hole and indeed just overhead (perhaps) at the end of the passage were traces of quite an ancient choke, all its surface covered with stalagmite (also surface of water hole), and all loose stones and gravel firmly sealed together.

The best thing to do now is to excavate with the big shovel a deepish hole at entrance and so to work a vertical surface up towards floor of chamber with enough head room for crawling on hands and knees. We should then be able to work much more in comfort and with better speed, and can tackle that doubtful floor safely. Progress it is now hoped will be quite satisfactory and even speedy. We have had a remarkable result for two hours work, but this is owed of course to the old packing partly and to good sand and stone for working in. I intend to get photos of hole in original condition, also as it is now and at intervals in progress. We were up there half an hour this afternoon and started home at 5.30 in a hard driving rain. R. Balch and Webb had put in five days at Ravine Hole Ebbor, had got in 20 ft, found an interred child's skeleton complete, a fragment of iron and at furthest point a 10 ft chimney with a fine branch stalactite grotto of small size. It is now closed in for the winter and we are getting authority to work there next season.

The bad weather continued. On 24 August, JHS and RNS cycled to Wells in the rain to make some purchases 'for my birthday', noting several swallets on the way where surface water was disappearing. In the afternoon they went to Nedge Hill Hole to take photographs and also enlarged the digging area to make it easier to work in. They found a stalactite curtain 6 in across broken clean off and several animal vertebrae and other bones. On the 25th, JHS's birthday, they cycled to Hunters Lodge and met Balch and Wheeler, then went to Priddy mines and photographed Wheel Pit and Priddy mines swallets, the latter was encroaching on the road badly. The third swallet in this group, 'the little swallet under pines' (Priddy Pool or Waldegrave Swallet?), was choked by another small fall of earth with little water running away. On the 26th, JHS changed his camera plates in the morning, and in the

Southern pool and reflections in front of Priddy (St Cuthbert's) mineries; half-plate (date unknown)

afternoon they worked at Nedge Hill Hole again with Barnes, making good progress in clearing out a lot of earth and 'rotten' limestone and finding another chip of pot and numerous modern bones. On the 27th they cycled to Wheel Pit Swallet, and on the 28th, to Wurt Pit in the morning and Devil's Punch Bowl and Bishop's Lot afterwards. Detailed measurements and rough plans were made at all three depressions.

29 August 1912

Changed plates and met Marle at the Vicar's Close at 11.30 a.m. Went through Chapter House, crypt, Lady Chapel, choir nave, cathedral library most interesting, cloisters and central tower where there are interesting tombs, capitals and brasses, fine view from the tower of all the hills and flats and Dulcote, a little water out towards Glastonbury. Dick and I biked on to Wookey Hole and worked a good bit in the three main chambers and passage getting ten photos in all, most of which turned out well. Bridge into no. 3 [chamber] was just submerged but we were able just to get in. Also took sandbank on N. side of no. 1, detail of terrace behind Witch, two corners of no. 2 and boulders in no. 3, also three on way out and got a good one of the ivy streamers and W. entrance while outside. A perfect roar of waters coming out at exit. While in first chamber we could fancy that we could hear a bumping sound at short regular intervals.

NEDGE HILL HOLE 30 August 1912

Nedge Hill Hole 10 a.m. to 3 p.m. Started by digging downwards at far end for 3 ft, hole nearly 6 ft now from floor to ceiling. The further way is now very puzzling, there is a thick clay soak at near end and exceedingly soft rotted limestone in floor at far end and vertically up towards triangular hole. There seems to be no definite channel onwards, seems hollow and loose under passage but would only go down to same depth I expect as in the 'porch'. Took three photos, strong draught taking off fumes through numerous crevices. Many traces of stalagmite in excavated earth, all split boulders *firmly* sealed together with it. To get on it may mean breaking through these, or penetrate through rotten limestone in direction of triangular hole (30°), down which we can see some 12 ft or so.

On the 31st they spent the morning in Bendall's Lot collecting ferns, and after lunch went to Sand Pit Hole near Priddy where they made measurements and a rough plan of the depression. They saw Balch at Rookham on their way back to Green Ore. Next morning, 1 September, they met Balch at Hunters Lodge and went with him via Wright's Piece to Charterhouse and Velvet Bottom to explore the mine workings there. On 2 September they packed up, Symes took the luggage to the station and they caught the train back to Bristol in the early afternoon.

The next visits to Mendip were on 7 September, when JHS cycled out to see the stone circles at Stanton Drew with Dick and Mortimer Savory, and 14 September, when he went by train to Burrington with Mortimer and 'two girls'. While 'waiting for the car to arrive', they discovered a small cave on the

21 September 1912. Frances Savory at Cross Quarry Cave on Wavering Down, quarried away in about 1925; photograph 5½ in × 3½ in

W. side of the gorge up beyond Rock of Ages nearly on a level with the latter. JHS suggests that this may have been Whitcombe's Hole, which had been excavated by Prof. W. Boyd Dawkins in about 1860, but, judging from the description and sketch, it seems more likely to have been Tunnel Cave. When the car arrived they 'started work' at the mud and scree choke at the bottom of Aveline's Hole, about 35 ft down, 'but could do nothing any further down, looks as if a great deal of work would be necessary to clear through. Was this hole where the skeletons were found?' On 21 September, he, Dick and Frances Savory walked westwards to Cross from Axbridge, examined cavities on the S.E. spur of Wavering Down, and took photographs of Coral Cave mouth, the flats and Crook's Peak. The weekly trips continued with two to Wookey Hole.

WOOKEY HOLE 28 September 1912

12.34 train to Wookey with John Allen. Arrived 1.58 and walked over the field via Glencot getting some grub for tea at Wookey Hole, left word for Barnes and Balch at the farm. We were expecting them about 6 p.m., took key and ladder and I filled lamp. We were ready to go in at 2.45. Did the three main chambers, nothing of any extra interest cropped up. Had left the ladder and camera gear at foot of W. series and came back. Water quite low enough to get into third chamber. I did the first climb, JA following with kit. Could not leave the ladder here for others as there was no fastening for it, so we put up a lighted candle to tell them we were up there, taking

the ladder on up for the next climb. The hole dug into sand bed at foot of Sentinel rift was deeper than I had imagined, over 5 ft. I backed up this rift hooking on the ladder and drawing it up. When near the top, as luck would have it, I hooked onto a stalagmite which brought the ladder close into the narrow angle of the fissure rather than well out, and in trying to get up JA let the camera, slung on his back, slip right round in front of him. The next thing was that he was stuck absolutely in the crack by the camera. He strained and pulled up against it and at last the strap gave way. Down went the camera bump, bump, bump down the rocks till with a final leap it settled in the wet sand at the bottom. We held our breaths during this, and when JA finished his climb I nipped down, hoping not to find it in too many bits; however we did not open the case till later. We finished the climb and made our way direct to the Grill, JA marvelling all the way at the wonders.

28 September 1912. Wookey Hole: the Grill, west series; half-plate

I had determined to get a good panoramic picture of the Grill, and having selected the right point and raised the camera a little, after several misfires, we exposed the left half. A draught kept the air very clear so we then exposed the right half. I had no viewfinder and afterwards was surprised to find that I had gauged the junction of the two halves to 1/16 in, thus getting full advantage of the whole length from end to end. I found that the camera did not appear to be damaged too much although the back was half out, and we spent all afternoon holding it in and covered with a cloth for fear all the plates would fall out. Also, the lens required to be pushed back in every now and then. We tied it up and went back to the 4½ pillars where I wanted to get an upright picture. This I obtained with very good lighting effect. Also discovered whereabouts of the two long inclined joined pencils in a small rift nearby. We went back to the main grotto and took four views of different points trying to specialize on lighting effect. Two of these were spoilt owing to one plate which broke in the fall. Scrambling through the horseshoe bend with care we took just one of some fine curtains although many other things could be done here. When we were half-way through with this we heard distant shouts from below and answered we were on the way down. We had been calling now at intervals for some time and at last the answer floated up. We could tell by the voices there were more than we had expected. We had just reached the foot of the ladder when Wheeler bundled through the tunnel. After some delay in unhooking the ladder which was on the wrong stalag-mite, we reached the low level without further incident, JA leading and myself giving him introductions from up aloft. First chamber lighted from the aperture and vice versa for Allen to see, then up through the Worm Cast Chamber where we had a little grub, and through the fissure getting a good photo of Allen and HEB higher up. A big flash was used which went off alongside my head and blew the lamp out which was perched on the other side. Turned sharp back along Oxbow and soon came up under the Spur and Wedge. I wanted to get a full exposure photo of this from the same position as of last attempt, but as I was placing camera on the tripod across the fissure out fell the lens and down 12 or 15 ft. By the mercy of providence it fell onto a small patch of fine sand and rolled away under the boulders which covered all the rest of the floor below us. As I was fixed, Barnes nipped down and got the lens, it was safe and sound but despite our efforts to stick it into the front these failed and we were forced to pack up and give up any idea of further photography. Altogether we had exposed eight or nine plates. Went up to the Conglomerate Ceiling and while I was registering the colours of the respective stones on a waste print, to try a colouring scheme, HEB showed JA round in the passages a little beyond. Barnes then suddenly warned us that the time was 8.05 p.m. so we all rushed for the entrance and, saying goodbye to the others who were going to dig a bit, we changed and legged it as hard as we could for the 8.30 train which we just caught nicely, getting a swill at the station.

28 September 1912. Wookey Hole: John Allen (below) and Balch climbing the Rift in the east series; half-plate

22 February or April 1913. Gough's Cave: bacon rasher curtains and pencil stalactites; whole-plate

MENDIP (Wookey Hole) 5 October 1912 (Saturday)

Started in the car at 9 a.m. with Mr and Mrs John Hassall and Wood, over the bridge, Brockley Combe, very glorious in autumn tints, up Burrington Combe without stopping. Turned to right to Charterhouse, stopped in the bend and wandered up over the workings and the ravines for an hour, obtained prickly and bifurcated hart's tongue ferns and found numerous other cave mouths, some filled in, some open and some like tunnels. Went back to the car and on to Cheddar, very slowly down the gorge which was truly magnificent in the morning light. We did Gough's Cave in the ordinary way, not going off the track this time; it was fairly wet.

Lunch at Cliff Hotel, then Wookey Hole. I showed them the way to the cave, very much less water running than last time. They were in advance, while I stayed behind and filled the lamp. They told me that HEB and another gentleman were up in the cave and just as I was leaving the yard, two ladies arrived down from the cave and one (Mrs Kentish) paid me the compliment 'Oh, there goes the guide with the lamp, look at him!' I overtook the others and as soon as Wood and I had put on boiler suits we marched in. Excavations at mouth on right bigger than ever. As soon as we got alongside the Spur and Wedge branch I gave a halloo and much surprised Balch and Kentish who were up there alone and were not expecting me. I scrambled up and shook hands, Kentish as usual was scrambling about and barking his shins, showering out interjections by the dozen, he was working round to expose Spur and Wedge from top which they were taking. We arranged to meet later and I went after the others.

We did the three chambers, although second was rather moist, the bridge into third chamber was now clear above water since last time. After getting back to the first again, Mr and Mrs Hassall went on out while I took Wood through the Worm Cast Chamber, showed him the aperture (which I had previously lighted through for them below), on up the fissure, Oxbow, under Spur and Wedge, up over latter, suspended floor, Conglomerate Ceiling and as far in as the rock passage beyond. Wood wanted to go further but time was going and the others were waiting, so we turned about. There was a solitary greater horseshoe bat in the last passage, a huge fellow, I took him down, he was very clammy cold and showed his teeth but hooked on again quite happily when I put him back. Passage narrow, we were kicking about very close under him in passing. Surely he would not be hibernating at this time of year. This is a very usual thing to have done in Wookey Hole, although often bats are seen flying round quite wildly, explanation? Came out and joined the others who had visited Hyaena Den.

A fortnight later, on 19 October, JHS wrote that he was 'now in communication with HEB about his WH [Wookey Hole] book'. There were only three more visits that year. The weekend of 23 and 24 November was spent with E. A. Baker based in Wells, when there was one trip to Wookey Hole and a long walk; the other two, in December, were concerned solely with preparation of the book. At Christmas JHS was incapacitated with ankle trouble and could not manage anything at all.

WOOKEY HOLE 23 November 1912

Walked to Wookey Hole from the station and found that Baker was alone up in the cave, so I took the rope ladder up and after changing at mouth at 2.30 met him doing the pools in the first chamber. After exchanging greetings we spent the rest of the afternoon in the three main chambers, trying for good lighting effects all the time. I did not do anything special that I had not done before. At 6 p.m. we went to the entrance and made an excellent tea in the waning daylight with a very varied menu, thanks to Baker.

At 6.30 HEB, Wheeler and a student named Bush arrived. We at once went up to the Spur and Wedge, Wheeler went through a little tunnel just below where we ourselves branched off and after a tight squeeze came out on the level of boulders below Spur and Wedge. I had not known of this passage before. We viewed Spur and Wedge from the board and lit it from several points, front, right and behind, this latter being very useful as it outlined both stones remarkably well, showing off their relative position. Unfortunately this was fogged with front light and fumes. Suspended boulders, Conglomerate Ceiling, they have excavated at the back of this to try and find a way into W. series but have not succeeded. Long passage up to the Crow's Nest, three of us struck away from the ordinary course and took an old stalagmite rift a little to the right which brings you out on the same level at the N. end of Crow's Nest Chamber, it is not far separated from main passage. We went right up to the Crow's Nest this time, right on until we could look out into the gloom of the glen and feel the air blowing on our faces. The nest must be annually increased as there are literally thousands upon thousands of sticks there, together with moss, wool and other soft stuff, giving a great contrast between the nest below and the ancient stream of old dry stalagmite streaming down the wall adjoining. This must be photographed with eggs in nest. This outlet is very nearly over the entrance to cave, very high up, and the whole of the Crow's Nest Chamber is roughly over the main passage so that we are not far away from the W. series. We had passed several greater horseshoe bats and spiders were also very plentiful, great shining rich brown things with long legs. We saw some of their cocoons which were very interesting, white fluffy little bags. We went down to the Guillotine which is by way of the drop you first come to, not the second towards Spur and Wedge. The Guillotine is very similar to the Spur, being a fragment dropped off a huge flake suspended in the rift just here. Just beyond, at a point called the Bats' Bridge, we collected together some bats of both varieties which were fairly numerous about here and photographed them. As usual they did not fly at our approach though they may be beginning to hibernate now, notwithstanding the fact that many were about outside while we were at tea. Their antics when taken in our warm hands and hung up in position were very laugh-

21 March 1913. Wookey Hole: first chamber showing the arch dividing the upper from the lower portion, with Wheeler and Barnes facing the Witch; whole-plate, limelight and flash

able, one little mite who perhaps had been tickled up a bit started to hug himself with his wings, occasionally stretching them out wide, then he would flap his little ears backwards and forwards and raise his eyebrows, he was most comical and we called him 'Little Titch'. One big bat hit me slap in the face on the way out of the cul-de-sac. Big fissure, lighted first chamber for Bush to see through aperture, packed up cameras and went from the entrance down to the farm.

There is a very welcome little pool in the first flow up in the Crow's Nest Chamber, we were *very* dry working over the sand. HEB discovered a third flow in this chamber even finer than the other two, am going to photograph it. While photographing the Spur and Wedge, Baker, with all our exhor-tation, would not keep still but moved about *freely*! so that in the plate he has about sixteen pipes. HEB had discovered in the Hyaena Den high up on the wall a crowd of bats hibernating, about seventy of them chock-a-block on about a couple of square feet of rock. When going back a second time to show Bush the third chamber we noticed a very interesting process going on. In one of the terraces behind the Witch there were several holes, when the water drops down from the high roof it splashes every drop out of these, but before the next drop comes the water has run in and nearly filled them, drained in from all the higher parts round, only all to be thrown out again when the next drop comes and so this goes on auto-matically for ever.

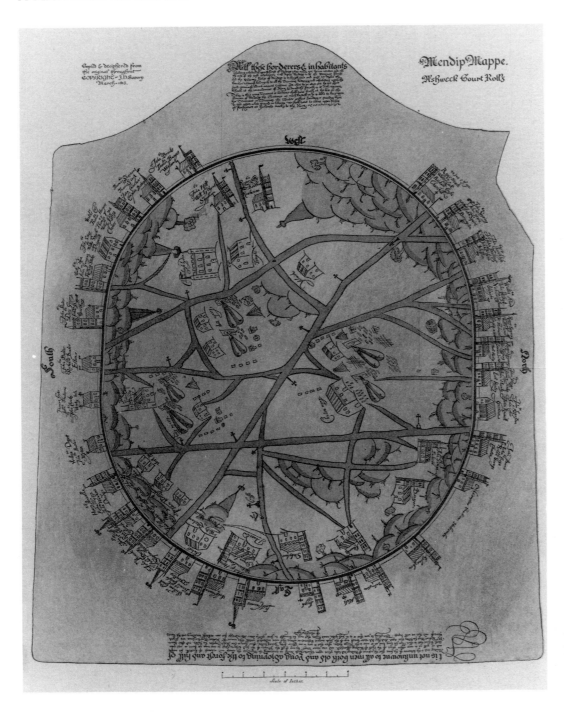

An ancient map of Mendip copied by JHS in March 1913 and published in the WNHAS Proceedings *for that year. Probably Elizabethan, it concerns old-time mining and commonage of the forest and hill of Mendip*

1913

1913 was JHS's most active year on Mendip, with thirty-eight diary entries of which eighteen describe caving trips, and eight of these to Wookey Hole. His copying of the old Mendip Mappe, which he had borrowed from Wells Museum on 24 November 1912, was dated March 1913 and published in the WNHAS Proceedings for that year. March must have been a busy time for him because he also spent two long weekends that month completing the illustrative material for Balch's Wookey Hole book, the first weekend being for John Hassall to do his artwork as well as for photography. Nor were these JHS's only projects in 1913. He took a series of fine photographs of the superb formations in Gough's (new) Cave at Cheddar on three visits in February and April, that were made into postcards for Goughs by Vandyck Printers. The same photographs, together with others by JHS of Cheddar and the Gorge, were used subsequently in pictorial guidebooks printed by E. W. Savory Ltd until at least 1930.

Unlike 1911 and 1912, JHS's summer holiday in 1913 was spent with Baker and two other cavers rather than with his brothers, and at a farm in Upper Milton rather than at Green Ore. In fact there seems to have been only one weekend stay at Green Ore that year. JHS had also started lecturing on caving, with lantern slides, and delivered one such lecture in 1912 at 'Camp, Salisbury Plain' and six in 1913 to Clifton College Scientific Society, Victoria Boys Brigade, Cirencester Baptist Guild, Clifton Photographic Club, Bath Literary and Philosophic Society and Bristol Naturalists' Society.

The first diary entries for 1913 describe an afternoon at Cheddar Gorge on 25 January, after a prolonged period of abnormally wet weather, and a visit to Banwell Stalactite and Bone Caves on 1 February. JHS offered to take photographs for Goughs on the first day, the reference to 'Vandyck gravure' concerning the then relatively new photogravure process for printing illustrations.

CHEDDAR 25 January 1913 (Saturday)

Started down by the 12.32 train with John Allen. Went straight up to Gough's Caves, left the road just under the Lion rock, and travelled up the gorge on the green slopes on the E. side, gradually climbing higher and higher. Just at this time the light and shade effects in the bends and corners of the gorge were delightful and we obtained a few photos from a considerable height. We went on up until cut off by coming to the end of the green at a 30 ft vertical cliff. Against the side of this a huge flake had split off all the way down and numerous stones are now wedged between the two. We turned about and looking S. a wonderful sight met our eyes, a wintry sun hanging over vast floods all over the flats and the slightly higher ground all chequered with rhines in full stream, the whole framed by the rocks on the sides of the mouth of the gorge. The Lion rock in the foreground and grand clouds passing overhead. A photo we took hardly did it justice. Going S. again we climbed a scree and from the higher level could see far away to the S.E. over Glastonbury Tor all the numerous knolls standing out conspicuously from the floods which extended right the way along. Beyond the Wedmore ridge the sun was shining on more water still, we could see a long narrow line over Sedgemoor or just W. of that. The light was getting weak but we clambered on to the head of the Lion rock, not much frequented as one has to step over a gap. From here again was an all round view, very good up the gorge.

We then descended to Gough's Caves and met E. Gough who had been fearfully watching us overhead. There was no time to see the caves but we introduced Vandyck gravure to him and offered to take some new views for him to publish. Gough told us that notwithstanding the record rainfall, they had not been prevented from entering the cave its whole length. Last Saturday it was as dry as usual but on the Sunday following, when the 'Springboks' S. Africans came for a visit, there was enough water in the first dip to have to put down timber for 50 ft or so, from the bridge at the specimen box to the fonts and as far again inwards.

BANWELL STALACTITE AND BONE CAVES 1 February 1913 (Saturday)

I had obtained permission from General F. H. Whitby last October but had not had a chance of doing anything till now, J. Allen was with me. Gen. Whitby was ready for us and immediately after donning our boiler suits we went up through the laurels to the deep cave, a slope down between two high walls leads to its entrance. In each case, however, the natural appearance of the entrance has been entirely altered by masonry. After going through the door a long flight of roughly built steps leads steeply down for 60–70 ft or so, we used a long rope all the way, attached to a stake at the entrance though this was hardly necessary. The drop was not bad but it was slippery, and after this one arrives at a natural platform and an iron stake here is fixed for attaching the rope ladder where one goes down a further 20–30 ft nearly vertically. This again I should think is not a bad rock climb minus ladder, and at the foot one bends low and goes through a tunnel about 12 ft long and at the other end is the head of another flight of steps, near the E. end of the main chamber of great size. It ceases to be a passage here and widens out on each side. On the way down we had passed a patch on the right of coral like stalagmite on the wall, not another pattern but the small rounded knobs similar to that in Coral Cave. We went down the steps and began to see overhead and on each side patches of the ordinary stalactite formations. Whitby tells me that it is said many pieces were carried off for the additional decoration of the Cheddar caves, and also from Burrington, and indeed there is much evidence here of breakage, a splendid flow in the bottom of the large chamber on the S. side has been hacked about dreadfully. This we took and right at the W. end came across Whitby sitting in the well-known Bishop's Chair built by a Bishop of Bath and Wells. The main part seems to be a natural piece of rock fallen from the roof, a half of a water pipe or pot-hole giving the half-round of the back and the seat built up from the ground with blocks of stalagmite etc. Behind are many huge detached blocks of stone with interesting looking cracks, fissures and passages beyond. This is the direction to work in should this cave have any communication with the Bone Cave. On the left facing up the steps, that is on the N. side, huge flakes have fallen away from the sides, still standing apart. On one of these were long streams of smooth stalagmite coming down, which stood out a bright white in the gloom against the black background, each crowned with a white knob. Along the whole length of the roof was a curious continuous line of round water pipes, depressions, rounded pots etc., and it may have been part of a formation such as this that formed the Bishop's Chair. All this, a wonderful chamber indeed, shone out as the light of the magnesium brightened for a while this unfrequented region of darkness. We took photos of the flow on the S. wall, two of the Bishop's Chair (one with Whitby sitting there), one of the huge flakes on N. side with stalagmite

flows and an unsatisfactory one of the whole chamber looking up towards entrance. This is one of those large dark voids with rocks of black which take an enormous amount of exposure. The bead like stalagmite would be worth getting in detail. Whitby would be willing for a good survey to be made of the two caves, plan and section, and this might prove most interesting to show their relations to each other. We spent some time coiling up the rope which was much too long and was fearfully tangled, then pulling up the rope ladder we made the best of our way to the entrance.

We proceeded to the house where we dropped all but the camera kit and went straight on (W.) to the Bone Cave. This is a small round chamber with one smaller side chamber also round, the floor is smooth and swept clear of all rubble, while round the sides in both places are numerous piles of artificially arranged bones. The columns of these in the centre 'as if supporting the roof' quoted by one Mr Rutter have long since vanished. One descends about 15 ft by a flight of steps with wall at the side into the main chamber, and at the foot just to the left several large stones in the floor surround a slight short slope leading to a blank. In the inner chamber the bones are thicker and some are arranged in patterns, all animals are still represented I suppose although Beard is said to have taken all the best specimens. Whitby told us that when this was open to the public every visitor used to take bones away with them, but soon tiring of them, the lawn of a little tea shop or pub belonging to an old man at the foot of the hill was absolutely littered with them. It has

1 February 1913. Banwell Stalactite Cave, General Whitby in the Bishop's Chair; half-plate

been closed for some time now but more people visit this than the deep cave. Just outside, in the centre of a small walled-in green with a walk round it, is a miniature make-believe stone circle with a mound in the middle and a triolith on the top, also the work of this eccentric Bishop, while scattered all over this part (the cave, circle, etc.) are inscribed marble slabs with quaint (some semi-religious) verses on. We returned to the house for tea and on the way Whitby pointed out the big bell over his stables which is one of the three which used to hang at Christon, it is inscribed to Jesus of Nazareth. One seems to be lost and the third was cracked by a too diligent man who was striking it last year. He showed us many Indian trophies and much old scraps of ecclesiastical glass let in round the windows of his house, most interesting figures etc. on many of them. I do not know where they came from. He showed us the tower in the wood eastwards, also built by the Bishop, and directed us across the fields to the road.

The next Mendip visit was on 15 February when JHS, his parents and Bryan Savory drove out to inspect a bungalow at Dursdon Drove/Rookham as possible accommodation 'for summer holiday', but it was 'rather dilapidated' and they were not impressed. The following weekend, on 22 February, JHS took a whole-plate camera and twelve plates on his first photographic visit to Gough's Cave. A week later came a long weekend with John Hassall at Wookey Hole.

GOUGH'S CAVE 22 February 1913 (Saturday)

Took the 12.32 equipped with whole-plate, stand and rucksack full of the necessaries, a good load. Purchased flash powder on the way down, must try and get recipe for this as I use much of it. Today all the expanse of floods over the flats had gone and they had resumed their normal appearance. The extraordinary long spell of rain had more or less stopped and today it was perfect. Picked up Gough at the Bath Arms! went up to the cave and had everything ready to start at 2 p.m. We got out at 6.30.

We thought it better to begin at the far end so made our way into the large chamber at once. We ascended the iron ladder. It was

1 February 1913. Banwell Bone Cave, stacked bones in the Bone Chamber; half-plate

22 February or April 1913. Gough's Cave: the Archangel's Wing in Solomon's Temple; whole-plate

my first visit here and, truth to tell, I was astounded by the profuse and rich formations which everywhere meet the eye, pile upon pile, all round you and overhead the roof covered with traceries, all imaginable and unimaginable forms are there. The Organ Pipes, a huge flow more like a forest of trees with great thick stems, this towers up many feet above one and is a beautiful mellow cream colour. The Archangel's Wing, a perfect stalactite joined to a perfect curtain. Pagoda shaped stalagmites, bosses, stoups, flows, basins, pencils and anemolites of every conceivable form, and most wonderful pools lined with crystallizations of all sorts. The eye wanders from one thing to another and is confounded with the beauty of it all. I can safely say that it is the richest patch not only in this cave, but anywhere that is yet known in Mendip. One gets but a poor idea below. I took the Organ Pipes from the extreme edge of the drop, but I found my lens was not nearly wide enough. However, I got a beautiful result showing the mellowness of it, but it may have to be taken again to be published. We then moved across to the Archangel's Wing on the left and here again got a successful photo. The cables were much in the way but the artificial light helped a good deal. While this was exposing I went into the little earthen chamber on the left, which shows promise of continuation by a small passage which Gough has entered, but it ends in a choke of earth which is thick all round, good clean sandy stuff. I secured a boss and a fine 12-in pencil from the floor which Gough gave me to take away. We then moved across to the right of Organ Pipes and took

two of the roof, more or less successful. Here again a passage, not earthen but covered in stalagmite, goes further on to a small grotto quite out of view of the public. I did not enter but Gough told me that the huge 'natural' stalagmite *placed* in the centre of platform before Organ Pipes had been secured from there. We got down to the front again and took two of the Pagoda stalagmites, both underexposed and require to be done again; they are splendid examples. We let off one big flash while the only party in were below.

The roof deserves a word; it is smooth and flat in most places due to the original passage of water, and all the limestone colouring shows well. Then has come a thin film of stalagmite to cover the whole, and only where there are cracks and seams have pencils and stalactites of rare beauty formed, and here and there one sees them in hundreds. To my mind the appearance of the barely covered rock is almost as fine. Two fine examples of anemolites on the right would be good to do in detail. We altered the lights according to how they came best, and then descended the ladder and took Niagara with the arc lamp which we left exposing while we explored further. This photo included the source of the flow and several fragments of rock gradually sealing into the surface. There is one curious little stalagmite on the left that stands up on a ledge just like a sentinel. Next we turned our attention to a huge fallen fragment weighing many tons just opposite. All is black and rocky here except one sparkling patch of white on the great boulder. It ripples down in lovely traceries to the over-

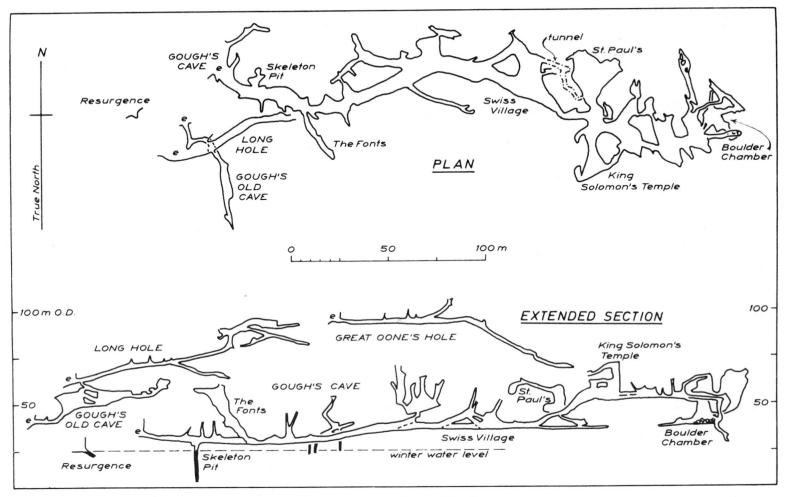

Plan and section of Gough's Cave and adjacent features, based on surveys by W.I. Stanton 1950–52

22 February or April 1913. Gough's Cave: wavy stalactite curtain near the Opera Box; whole-plate

hanging ledge where fine little curtains have formed. All this has a fine background of dark scree running up into the chamber of the broken floor. Thither we now turned our steps and got a fine photo of the only sparkling white curtain and stalactite which hang side by side in the roof here, the latter running high up into a fissure. More smaller but good anemolites here. We then went into the other large chamber [St Paul's] and tried for a good light effect with bright light on the distant pools and dark curtains in foreground, but lens would not take the different focus and it was underexposed. All formations very red and brown here, hopelessly underexposed. We exploded the arc lamp so could take no further ones here. We finished the twelve plates by taking two of the reflections in the pools left and right of the fine mellow stalagmites standing in the (artificial) pools, underexposed but good results with deep shadows in the background. Results well repaid trouble of taking the whole-plate down. They are really some of the best cave photos I have seen even though it is a show place. We considered various other points for another time and then packed up and went to the entrance without delay.

Here Gough showed me the little leaded windows out of Hannah More's Cheddar cottage, they are very quaint; cottage has just been tiled instead of thatch, pity! Had a few words with A. G. H. Gough and got more or less on business terms. Went and had a drink with E. Gough and then had a rattling good tea at the Cliff Hotel. After this I still had 45 minutes before the 7.55 train so took a 20-minute stroll in the gorge,

and I can safely say this is one of the most impressive 20 minutes I have spent. As I left the hotel the lights in the cottage windows came into view all reflected well in the mere. Cheery voices were coming from the cosy rooms there behind the drawn blinds, then on in the darkness was heard the roar of the issuing streams. Soon this died away behind me. I was leaving the last of the cottages where an occasional dog's bark sounded and entering the silence of the gorge itself. All was for the most part absolutely still, an occasional breeze rustled the bushes high up on the cliffs or started a trickle of scree downwards. There was no moon but a sky as starlit as could be; it silhouetted the cliffs which seemed to hem one in, towering up there 500 ft. This accentuated the brightness of the myriads of stars. On ahead in a break in the cliffs the Great Bear tilted up was pointing its 'tail' stars downward through the narrow slit; it held my attention for some time. It seemed good to be alive and see such a sight as all this. Shooting stars were frequent, appearing and disappearing with startling swiftness. Here I stayed for some while, with no sound but an owl now and then. At last as time was short I reluctantly turned about, trying to pierce the gloom up into those cliffs. When I got near the mouth a break in the cliffs showed me a wonderfully bright planet far off over the moors which one could faintly define. This one outshone all the others and actually cast a visible shadow of myself on the road. Gradually as I went downwards the ordinary village sounds made themselves heard, the roar of the waters, voices, lights again and soon I was back at the hotel, picked up my load and was stepping it out through straggling Cheddar to the station. I could not resist going into Mr Small's for the usual cheese as I passed. He tells me much comes from Cheddar itself and all from within a very small radius, 5–10 tons per annum being usual. Caught the last train home.

28 February 1913 (Friday)

Friday to Monday with John Hassall doing the three restoration drawings for [Balch's] book. Met JH at station and went straight on down to Wells. I had cameras, maps etc., which were all to be used in connection with the book.

WOOKEY HOLE 1 March 1913 (Saturday)

We got off in good time and went straight to entrance, not going in very far. JH immediately set to work on the interior near entrance, where a hearth was reconstructed, and after this the exterior near entrance, showing nature of cliff. We then had a very substantial lunch of bread and cheese, cake and beer, and then went round into the bottom of the gorge for the Hyaena Den drawing. This we worked out very well. We went round the E. side of cliff and visited Badger Hole, where those animals had just recently been very active. JH dug out a rotten goat's skull, much *breccia* here and signs of longer passages. Then down to the Rhino Hole with its bank of excavated earth in front of entrance, otherwise not of much interest. Then to the Hyaena Den top entrance and we slid down to bottom level. It has not altered much since Boyd Daw-

kins' time. We crawled into the low part right to the end where the three of us could just stand up. This is where the bad air occurred (the only time known) when HEB had to pull out the man who had fallen, by his legs. It is a bad backwater. An interesting record seen here was that a shell or film of stalagmite had formed over Boyd Dawkins' pick marks and the face of his work. Some was procured and averaged about 1/64 in thick. This was since 1864? Wheeler had been there a few days before and driven his pick through the apparent bed rock into more *breccia*. This was tried on the strength of a sentence (Hyaena Den) in *Cave Hunting*; there is yet something good to be got there. Of course HEB made some good finds there after BD departed.

Having finished the third sketch and got

Wookey Hole: John Hassall's restoration, based on archaeological finds, 'Interior of the Late-Celtic Cave Dwelling', drawn for Wookey Hole, Its Caves and Cave Dwellers *(1914).*

numerous suggestions, we wandered along the canal and here we found several dead Miller's Thumbs in weed on bottom, with their shiny underneath parts turned upwards. We wondered if these had come out of the cave and looked at their eyes which seemed to be peculiar, though this might only have been from putrefaction. HEB had preserved other things found in all these waters. The group of bats had gone from the Hyaena Den and we could not see them elsewhere. By this time it was getting dusk so, leaving much of our stuff at Adlam's, we made our way home. Balch and Marle came in in the evening and we settled for the next day. Took some food bones away from the pile inside cave doorway, and when we had walked as far as the first chamber, we lit up near the river with magnesium ribbon. There was a great stir of mud and a fish, the first one seen in the cave, shot away. Light has a peculiar effect on the blind fishes of underground. There is a long fissure E. of the water exit, where Balch sent a boy down once and he went so far that he had to be called back; it is too narrow for a man. I threw a match forward 30 or 40 ft and it goes still further. There is another hole low down under the roots of tree E. of canal. This is only a small triangular hole but it goes in some little way on the left. It is hardly worth excavation and is far from the general direction of the cave.

WOOKEY HOLE 2 March 1913 (Sunday)

Cathedral in morning. Bike to Wookey Hole with Balch, John Hassall, Marle and Hodgson, a student and cousin of JH's, left bikes at Adlam's. We did the passage from near Crow's Nest to cliff entrance. Big stones are kept over inner end to prevent people coming in. We came across some big pieces of fresh meat 40 ft in from exit, probably lamb as no small bones were showing, all had disappeared by the same time on the next day, probably foxes or perhaps badgers. We walked again round the head of Wookey Hole gorge for Hassall's benefit, then across the old track which runs over second chamber up to Higher Pitts farm, it is an old freehold and is marked on large scale map at 2–3 acres. Then into Smoakam wood, this is renowned for the specially large size of its rabbits. This wood, like Ham wood further E., is peculiar as it has one rock (limestone) on one side and another (Dolomitic conglomerate) on the other, it is not very many yards across. Near the top Balch showed me the limestone (bed rock) showing as an outcrop, looks like the top of an ancient cliff and is probably the W. side of the old limestone ravine seemingly filled in later with the conglomerate. The limestone probably descends here 400 ft, taking the cave [Wookey Hole] into consideration which is all in conglomerate, at this one point this is well shown, E. side of conglomerate is not very far out E. of Smoakam wood.

HEB also tells me that the sixth level of the river in Wookey Hole now trying to form, just beyond third chamber, is the reason for the springs (two) rising at Glencot only 20 ft from Axe itself. The passage between the fourth and the third chamber is called 'Holy Hole' by ancient writer, Balch found names there when he went in on raft,

Wookey Hole: John Hassall's drawing, based on finds of bones and artefacts, of 'The Goatherd of Wookey Hole'. In these early remains may lie the origin of the ancient legend of the Witch of Wookey, a wicked old woman who lived in the cave and who was supposedly turned into stone by a good monk from Glastonbury

probably written before dam at exit raised head of water. One could then walk some way along on the old stepping stones in the bed. This could still be done if all the sluices were running free, canal has been in use for very many years without repair and may be cleaned next Whitsuntide, if so when water has gone we shall see Holy Hole and right along, under the old conditions. We discovered some *breccia* in the Badger Hole which is very promising, quite a good bit of it about shoulder high. JH pulled out a rotten goat skull from just inside one of the holes. While looking at the fish in the first chamber [1.3.13], we noticed a regular looking stump of stone which was just within reach and when pulled out proved to be 18 in long stalactite, very stout with several points and I noticed at once must have been knocked off years ago from the remaining stump seen above the traceries behind Witch. I carted this home on a later date (Easter). During our work this spell when about the gorge we heard several minor rock falls and trickles of earth, the gradual action of wind, frost and rain which is acting on the face of the cliff and making it recede. I noticed to the right of and over the W. rock entrance a huge detached flake standing upright but separated from bed rock, not very much is needed to send this going. Near Hell Ladder there is a big boulder only just wedged and quite ready to slide down onto the path. The only place showing dip of conglomerate strata is just to the right inside Hodgkinson's cart entrance, shows well dipping south, there may be examples on other side of gorge. In going up to the Spur and Wedge this last time I did the under cut,

very tight, it brings you out in bottom of Boulder Chamber below Spur, jackdaws were there in crowds, very busy but as yet no eggs. All round Hell Ladder is good for finds and excavation and has not yet been touched.

HEB told me about the movement and crushing down of a great boulder near the pebble ledge at entrance to Boulder Chamber in Eastwater. The man he was working with (at the original excavation) was pushing forward on his stomach under a huge boulder supported at each side by two smaller ones, all of a sudden Balch standing behind was horrified to see the big chap suddenly start *crushing its way* through the smaller ones on to the man's back. It came to rest just as it touched his boiler suit and when HEB asked if he had felt anything the man replied 'yes I thought you touched me on the back', he had neither seen nor heard what was going on.

WOOKEY HOLE 3 March 1913 (Monday)

Wookey Hole again with Balch at 9.30 a.m., anxious to get the Witch well for a frontispiece. First one, we tried to add to illumination by putting ribbon on top of powder but the result was ludicrous, a perfect rain of flying shreds of ribbon which completely spoilt the plate; second fairly good. We walked through to third chamber, trying to satisfy ourselves as to best positions for taking the three chambers for Balch's book. We then ventured the wholeplate camera up into the W. series, rather risky. Measured the Sentinel on this occasion, 5 ft 8 in on the rift or E. side and 5 ft 4 in on the higher side.

3 March 1913. Wookey Hole: John Hassall at the Spur and Wedge, east series; half-plate

An interesting point shown in my photo had escaped my notice before; a good large stone had fallen and slid down the slope towards foot of Sentinel. It had come to a stop 6 in from base, another 6 in would have destroyed the Sentinel for ever; the stone is now sealed in. We took camera through the horseshoe twist and tried to get a general view of next grotto and the joined pillar from roof to saddle back; 6 in Racy [lens] is bound to be used for latter. Both were very badly fumed. I went just as far as Grill and we then returned and took the half-plate only up to the Spur and Wedge where we got an excellent negative for the book, this after about six attempts; J. Hassall figures in this and it is lighted in four places. Suspended Boulders was much overexposed and I had moved, must try this again as I want to figure in at least one of the plates. We went as far as jackdaw's nest and back, no eggs and not much sign of bats except on this occasion I spotted a long-eared bat, the first ever seen in the cave, it was just beyond the Conglomerate Ceiling. The horseshoe bats chase other species out it is thought. We got back to the entrance at about 2.30.

4 March 1913 (Tuesday)

Caught the 9.30 a.m. home. This journey had been more useful from Hassall's point of view than from mine, though I was jolly thankful to at last have one of the Spur and Wedge. As I was leaving in the morning I heard a terrific hullabaloo and found about six of the students (it was their holiday) doing 'caving practice', roped together with dressing gown girdles in all costumes. I saw them first on a very elastic mattress all up in line while their leader Guy Hodgkinson had managed to struggle through the bars at the foot of the bed, then aiming at a mountain of bedding on a chair, then a tight squeeze round some drawers. Then they shot across the close and up through the chaplain's little peep window, after that I know not where. It was all most laughable. They had been prompted by the fact that the chaplain Marle had raised a wave of enthusiasm through the college for caving and a party were that day visiting Eastwater. It was wet and they were very ragged on getting out. They got into 380 ft Way and struggled into the tight right angles rift at end, then, thinking they had come to the end of the main passsage, they started to look for the 380 ft Way and failed! Only on getting out did they think what had happened. They had not had enough (5 hours) but they went on to Lamb Lair and this they report to be entirely closed by fallen earth, not even the rabbit hole left at foot of entrance shaft. Am trying to get a government grant to clear this and renew windlass. The same party tried Eastwater a week later and this time safely reached the Second Great Rift Chamber and returned. Marle has run up rather a reputation now.

JHS went down to Wookey Hole again on his own three weekends later at Easter, for the purpose of completing the photography in the cave that was required for the book. The reason why the camera exposure times were so long on Good Friday was that limelight was being used for illumination, and photographic emulsion was far less sensitive to this

The Witch of Wookey (frontispiece in Wookey
Hole, Its Caves and Cave Dwellers, *1914);*
whole-plate

'He chauntede out his godlie booke,
He crost the water, blest the brooke,
Then – pater noster done –
The ghastly hag he sprinkled o'er:
When lo! where stood a hag before,
Now stood a ghastly stone.'

   *(from a 1756 ballad by Henry Harrington,
a Bath physician)*

79

light than to the more customary magnesium ribbon. The interpretation of the noises in the cave must have been very satisfying, because they had been a source of mystery and debate for several years.

WOOKEY HOLE 21 March 1913 (Good Friday)

Went down to Bubwith very loaded up with two cameras and much kit; the others, HEB, Barnes and Wheeler arrived soon after 9 a.m. It was to be limelight this visit and we were going to tackle the three main chambers. We struggled up with the cylinders, having to make several journeys, and at last all was ready in the first. We took various choices of positions. I had Biggs' 6 in very wide angle lens and when the light burned up I saw the cave as I had never seen it before. Every detail showed in the bright light, right over to the sandbank. We used long elder wands and wired candles to them for holding up high and getting the exact field of view on screen. When all was ready we exposed and made up our minds for a 2 hour exposure. Barnes and Wheeler went off into the W. series and I stopped and chatted to Balch. I had taken a 4½-in condenser down and placed it on a little heap of sand in front of the two acetylene hand lamps to give a good powerful ray which we used for dispelling bad shadows where they were not wanted. One strong one from the Witch was quite invisible now. We did this in all three chambers, and when held in front of limelight the condenser shot a dazzling beam across the black space. Time dragged slowly and we finished up with one

big flash behind the Witch and another behind S. shoulder by river, Barnes and Wheeler standing in for this. There was the usual good natured jibing going on and many cutting remarks when Barnes gracefully slithered down the W. drop.

We then proceeded into the second chamber at about 12.15. As before, we placed candles out all round for focussing and framing. While Wheeler was down near the further arch he all of a sudden yelled 'hark, hark', and at the very same moment I had heard a rumbling separate from the resounding of voices so almost knew what to expect. Immediately there was a dead silence on our part and everyone listened breathlessly. There was a low musical rumbling going on somewhere beyond Wheeler. This was exactly at 12.30 and I could hear it well from the top of the terraces. I made a note of the time at once. The noise gradually increased in volume and then started to die away again, till only an occasional murmur could be heard, then again dead silence. There was much discussion at the time but we collected the candles and started to expose all along the top, four cameras and limelight going well, also condenser and two acetylenes again, another 2 hours! This chamber seemed to be fuming badly and I did not hope for the best at the time. In an hour's time at 1.30 we had all more or less subsided into a somnolent condition, when out of the darkness ahead again that noise in exactly the same way as before. Without a second thought we all seized our candles and rushed pell mell down into the third chamber, where we collected at the sand pile and listened with

21 March 1913. Wookey Hole: second chamber, 70 ft high; whole-plate, limelight and flash

all our ears to the noises which had just reached their height. We sat around the sand pile and made immediate notes of our impressions. Balch said they were like cymbals but afterwards agreed with me that it more resembled a slow intermittent roll on a rather high-pitched orchestra drum, or again perhaps the twanging again and again of a double bass string. Starting faintly, gaining volume until the chamber resounded, then dying away as they had come, lasting from beginning to end about 4 to 5 minutes. They were extremely musical. We finished the second chamber with a 20 second candle (5/-!), which Barnes crawled along with on the sandbank on the other side of the water. We had much ado to keep out of its way. I stood on bridge the while and my reflection shows well. I was able to get full height well. We took short walks to pass the time.

Then on again to the far end of the third chamber, where we looked back, ranging our cameras along the wall. Black was very bad here, hazy too. Whole-plate camera was quite close to the water, limelight further round and acetylene too. We all sat on the sand-bank up to the W. and by way of new variety and to pass the time, we did string, coin and other puzzles and tricks, even descending to asking riddles, chestnuts too some of them. We threw stones large and small into the river and noticed that when thrown just to the right of the last arch the larger ripples seemed to run under a lip of rock along the water's edge, just touching it and producing an occasional note very rich and musical at times, like water rippling under the lip of an inverted glass. We had all

been quiet for a while when all of a sudden there was a gurgle. This was quite enough for me and I rushed across in front of the cameras, put the cap on and picked up the condenser, and in a moment was sweeping the river with a strong beam. We were familiar enough with the noises by now to know what to expect. My idea was to catch the slightest motion of the water and also to put under a strong light the exact locality from whence they appeared to be coming. The time was 5.30 and the general style of these sounds with their resounding effects through the chamber was quite similar to the previous ones, but now we were right on the spot and we could hear something in addition at the lip of rock. Through apparently a foot or two of rock was the gurgling and sucking of moving water, as if it was being buffeted about and struggling hard in a confined space, while seemingly further into the rock to the left we heard faintly the low-toned thud, thud, thud of similar nature to that heard on a previous occasion. It was difficult to say if (on any of the three times) the water was struggling upwards or downwards. Of course, the three times exactly corresponded with the three times the mill sluice was touched during the day, 12.30 closed, waterfall then comes into action, 1.30 opened, 5.30 closed again. What exact effect this had on the river beyond the third chamber is most difficult to conjecture. Now in addition to the noises, under the limelight we noticed by looking carefully that there were a series of concentric ripples coming from just to the right of the arch from a spot only a few feet from where the arch meets the water on that side.

23 March 1913. The River Axe emerging from Wookey Hole, showing the sluice; whole-plate

21 March 1913. Wookey Hole: third chamber, Balch and JHS; whole-plate, limelight and flash

This happened to be the exact spot that the note came from when stones were thrown in, and it would appear that under this lip of rock there is some communication, perhaps only small, with the cavities over the arch. Since water always finds its own level it is difficult to say what forces it so high. Again, are these noises due entirely to action of the sluice, and would these particular ones have occured before the canal was made thirty years back? Noises *were* heard in ancient times. The height of the water on this occasion was average. Between 1.30 and 5.30 we had been watching the water rise very gradually over the partly submerged boulders in the river.

We finished exposing the third chamber by a big flash behind the sand pile, then carted all the kit back to the first chamber where we tried two more of the Witch, this time illuminating the dark patch behind head with a candle on the higher level. The second time Balch took us photographing and got quite a passable photo of the chamber from near the entrance, showing the photographers. Balch pointed out a second good profile of the Witch from near the big column. Also noticed that the big column is being formed by a single short pencil (2 in), which is fairly spouting water like a tap going strong, not dropping always downwards but varying first one side then the other. Balch says it is as if under pressure. There is another island stalagmite forming beside the old one in the pools between first and second chambers. I noticed that no bedding [bedrock] whatever shows in second chamber. When walking outside during the day Wheeler and Barnes reported having heard and seen the tail end of quite a

reasonable cliff fall. Wheeler reported twenty-eight bats near Guillotine, probably from the Hyaena Den. Got out about dark at 6.30, said goodbye at Adlam's and home.

22 March 1913 (Easter Saturday)

Wells early in morning, very dull, Dawkes and Partridge re slide, Vicar's Close, HEB. His four negatives hopelessly underexposed, spotty and no good at all. This gave me the dumps as I was getting a *little* tired of photography in Wookey Hole. Fixed up much line work for book. Back to Ebbor, lunch early, strolled out afterwards. Took photos of Arthur's Point and tried three times with broad angle lens for good cave gorge photo and got it in very poor light. Rain simply pelting down. View shows all that is necessary. HEB tells me of an ancient exit valley between E. Milton and W. Milton, I must get him to show me this when a chance comes.

On Easter Sunday JHS managed to get a good photograph of the gorge at Wookey Hole in bright sunshine, before going to morning service in Wells Cathedral and then visiting Balch. In the afternoon he cycled to Priddy via Hope Wood and then to Red Quar and Green Ore, where he had tea with the Symes. He went to evening service in the little church at Wookey Hole and then had supper with the Adlams.

WOOKEY HOLE 24 March 1913 (Easter Monday)

Wookey Hole again. HEB arrived at 10.30

24 March 1913. Wookey Hole: looking up the slope to the Witch from near the river in the first chamber, Webb, Balch and small lad; whole-plate

a.m. We went to ask Lee if canal could be emptied but found it was impossible, though it may still be done at Whitsun when the canal has to be cleaned. This has not been done since it was built thirty years ago. Webb and his brother arrived a little later. Took in the whole-plate and got a very successful view of first chamber from the S.E., getting whole of N. side of chamber and slopes down to river as well. Went with the half-plate up to Suspended Boulders to have yet another try as none had been successful. I sat up for it, taken from Wedge; then I took Balch lighted only from the rear, a very weird effect that we had noticed when doing the first exposure. Went to see if the group of bats were on Guillotine but they had gone; also the jackdaws are not laying up there yet. We had our grub in the Slab Chamber in quietness and drank from the little pools. Put rocks back over the hole leading to cliff entrance, when we noticed a huge mass of standing rock detached from cliff and poised just ready to be precipitated into the valley below. Went back to first chamber and took it again from entrance (like Bamforth's), Balch sitting for this by the pools (Webb and small persevering lad stood for first one). Took Witch again for luck as we want a good one for the frontispiece; out at 4.30.

This seems to have completed the photography for the Wookey Hole book, because on the next trip into Wookey Hole, on 1 June, no camera was taken, and the first proofs for the book were checked on 15 June. Before then, however, were the two other photographic visits to Gough's Cave on 1 and 11 April, which get just the briefest mention, and a trip to Dolbury and Burrington Combe on 25 May.

CHEDDAR 1 and 11 April 1913

Gough's Cave, two cameras first day, good photos of Niagara etc. Second day, good again, given good specimens by A. G. H. Gough, first swallows seen over the pools S. of Nailsea station. Gough's order now complete (17.6.13), cards look extremely well, quite new views among them.

DOLBURY AND BURRINGTON 25 May 1913 (Saturday)

C. E. Atkinson, Father and self, car 2.15

24 March 1913. Wookey Hole: JHS on the Boulder Bridge, east series; half-plate

22 February or April 1913. Gough's Cave: the Peal of Bells; whole-plate

1 April 1913. Gough's Cave: Sinnock climbing up from the lower boulder chamber; half-plate

p.m. Brockley Combe to Dinghurst, not much left of this camp, good rocks along the road here, quarried I think. Climbed Dolbury, alive with rabbits, grand views all around, boats in the Channel. Up to the summit, then on S. of Mendip Lodge wood, caught a grass snake in the wall here, then we came across a grand swallet. Half-way along the wood a 40 ft cliff, good strata and old cracks and holes, most interesting all round and good for further examination and excavation. Three different soaks, a good stream running into middle one from which we pulled out mud teeming with dragonfly larvae. Made our way across to middle path W. brooklet and came across other small springs and streamlets, down across W. brook then up to [Goatchurch] cave entrance. We found it broken open and walked down with matches to the end of the railing, path stepped in [cut into] stalagmite, good formations at once on entering cave, bosses and flows, then the ways divide and go downwards giving much promise. Must do this sometime, strata shows well underground, active swallet immediately below Goatchurch has been excavated.

WOOKEY HOLE 1 June 1913 (Saturday)

12.30 train self. Atkinson, J. A. Brown and Prideaux on motor bikes, arranged to meet in village, walked from station with rucksack. Atkinson was there to the minute at 2.30 but the other two came nearly an hour late; very heavy rains all round Bristol though quite dry down there. This gave us two time to go up to the gorge and river exit, it was dark and gloomy under the trees, the whole glen being beautiful, returned via Hyaena Den. Gave them up after a bit and started for the cave, but we heard a hum and before we had reached the gate they spun round the corner, much chaff etc., returned to farm and started again. I exhibited my wardrobe, costumes for all, candles etc. at the cave mouth, with Brown and Prideaux things became quite hilarious. We had no camera so were able to get on quickly. Through to the third chamber where we put the lights out and made some good gurgles with stones thrown into river. Back to second chamber where we let off an incandescent Roman Candle (6d). The sparks went up with a big smack to the highest part of the roof, illuminating it well, some fine stalactites, then falling right back alight to the mud. Back into first chamber where we lit off a red flare on top of the Witch's head, the resulting glare was very weird and fine as the gloomy fumes floated away over the river. Here Prideaux bade us a very sad farewell because of his knee, and found his way back to the entrance where he explored the ravine and went over the paper mill. I did the climb, hooked the ladder up and soon the other two were up alongside. We went straight on up and as I looked towards the Sentinel in the light of the first candle up, I thought in the gloom that it looked out of vertical. I thought no more of it as I was sitting at the top of the second climb helping the others up. When we were all on top we moved along to the Sentinel and to my horror I found it broken 6 in from the base and leaning its whole length against the rock on the other side. It was 10 in out of the vertical and the broken ends were not even separated, while the long white pencil stalactite looked as if it would never have anything else to live for. I stood gazing at the catastrophe for a long while and the others could not make out what was wrong. I wrote Balch at once and he has since been able to stay while a plaster collar was setting and it now stands upright again. My first thought was that the moment had come after all the ages when the leverage had become too great and it had at last given in, but Balch says that it would still just stand up alone on the stump showing that its 5 ft 8 in rift side held no great stress. A theology student has just owned up that he took hold of it when up there and it snapped. The marvel is that it was not all in fragments down at the bottom of the rift.

We made our way slowly up to the Grill where I scrambled through to show them it *was* possible. We examined some of the large clay balls and then went back to the first chamber without further incident. Continual passage over the tight bits has gradually knocked off many of the finer points. Across the Worm Cast Chamber, up the fissure round to the Spur and Wedge, Atkinson getting warm, Suspended Boulders, Congolmerate Ceiling and then to our horror we found we had a bare 45 minutes for the train.

Rushed out, washed at Adlam's and rushed up to the village club where we had a good tea. Prideaux and I had to catch train to Winscombe, so Atkinson spun off solo and Jimmie Brown took us two up on his motor bike (Scott) and side car. It failed on the steep bit in and, not having any brakes in particular it started running backwards,

and I hopped off and sent Jimmie into fits when I asked him if he expected me to stop it; he seemed helpless so we gently subsided into the hedge. In the end we got our train to the minute and went up the line to Winscombe, a fine evening, leaving Jimmie to go home with my rucksack for company.

JHS spent that night and the following one at Winscombe with Prideaux, and on Sunday 2 June they and Wigglesworth walked up to the tops of Wavering Down and Crook's Peak. He returned to Bristol on Monday morning. Two weekends later he stayed with the Symes for two nights. On 14 June he did a round tour to Masbury Castle, Beacon Hill, Gurney Slade, had tea in an old inn near Old Down, then to Emborough pond and Nedge Hill, seeing a record number of barrows (burial mounds) along the way. The following day he walked with Mr Symes in the morning and, in the afternoon, checked the first proofs of the Wookey Hole book with Balch and then cycled with him to inspect a deep swallet pit above Seldon's. They also took measurements of the barrows at the calamine workings just west of Bendall's Lot. There were three more day trips before JHS's summer holiday, the first with Clifton College Scientific Society to Dolbury and Burrington, the second with Thompson and Aspell from the USA to Wookey Hole. On 23 August he went to Cheddar.

CHEDDAR 23 August 1913

We three [JHS, EWS – father, T. Mostyn – artist] started off in the morning, in good time and a perfect day, fresh, bright sun and

*22 February or April 1913. Gough's Cave: tall
red stalagmite cascade on the wall of St Paul's;
whole-plate*

large clouds. We made our first stop at Plumley's Den where TM spent some time making a sketch of the Rock of Ages opposite. All his sketches today were only for picture ideas so he took only bits of detail. Went straight to Cheddar, where we stopped for lunch a little way down, near the little ravine branching in from the W. Here TM made some more sketches. I have never seen Cheddar looking finer, from weather effects. Meanwhile I went on down with EWS and the car to the Long Hole by the water-works and here EWS let me down the 60° slope with my 60 ft rope, and although he was several yards inside the cave, round the first two curves and right at the head of slope, the rope proved too short. I took the rope as a precaution but soon found that I could get on fairly well without, so finished that way. I had my acetylene lamp and could see that the rift was enormously high and but a few feet broad. A good iron gate from the entrance reposes at foot of slope, a little further on two huge fallen boulders cut right across, over which you must climb, and after this the floor starts to rise a little and ends in a narrow crack at the top of a steepish bit. It was here that I nearly crocked my ankle badly by slipping down 8 or 10 ft when trying to back and knee up to see if there was any way on over a likely shoulder 18 ft or so up. I found afterwards that there did not seem to be one, by looking across from the entrance slope with magnesium ribbon. My slip was due to the remarkably greasy state of the walls, for which the cave is noted. No stalagmite forms here which is hard and crystalline, but the same substance accumulates on the sides of the rift, and

remains in a wet clayey state, never hardening. One or two poor instances of cock-combing at inner end seemed slightly firmer, but were very rotten and not crystalline, easily breaking to the touch. Elsewhere, right up to the entrance in fact where huge initials disfigure the place, I could easily push my hand in almost up to the wrist. The usual features of stalagmite *flows* show badly here and there (*no* pendants or columns), but there is no sharpness of edge anywhere. Mostly white, but in places brown. I brought away some of each and when the water had dried out though in as compact a ball as I could make it beforehand, it is now extremely light and crumbles easily.

On starting to return, I heard distant voices and from what seemed far above me I could make out the lights of EWS and TM. For their benefit I sat on the fallen boulders at bottom and lit up with magnesium ribbon in their view, obscuring direct light with my own body and the boulders. The effect to them was very weird and particularly struck TM who had never seen anything like it. I appeared to be the wizard of the cave and as a result he painted me the picture of the Long Hole as a birthday present for the 25th. After climbing out, one has to be careful in places, and appearing to the amusement of the others as a mass of white plaster, I packed up and we made our way down to the village.

JHS's caving holiday was from 5–14 September, staying with E. A. Baker (Blackheath), A. H. Blake (London) and R. H. Chandler (Belvedere) at Manor Farm, Milton. They explored caves on four days.

5 September 1913 (Friday)

Went down by evening train on the 5th, taking bike, all ropes and tools and running to a good deal excess. HEB and Chandler met me at station and we hoisted our joint luggage on to a carriage, going straight on to Mrs Withers, The Manor Farm, Upper Milton. We stopped in town, made some purchases and then in the dark and rain made our way on bikes to our diggings, where there was a good cheery fire and a good meal waiting for us. Chandler is a geologist and we had much in common to talk about. I had arranged a few days ago for the three men to go with me to Lamb Lair, there joining some of the Bristol Spelaeological [Research] Society men who had been working there at clearing a good bit just lately. Baker and Blake were in Wells for that night waiting for their rooms to be at liberty here, so we two were alone.

We visited our bedrooms to unpack, it is a large rambling house and not all used. Our rooms were quite comfortable but not too scrupulously clean. In many of the rooms (you go about all over the place opening from one room into the next) there was a stratum of cats, mats, hats, kittens, dust, dogs, muddles, food and guns, though altogether there was nothing much to take exception to, the whole place having a rambling old-fashioned appearance, huge kitchens and sculleries with large covered-over fireplaces, ovens and boilers. Here you were always falling over young turkeys and other poultry. But when we turned in for the night, what excitement! Never had I seen so much livestock in any bed; in the folds there

were literally lines of them. We attacked them with soap, an infallible method, and caught dozens of them. The sheets were covered with large black and brown patches too, and having mustered up courage we went in force to lay a formal complaint, only to be assured that the sheets were perfectly clean but the 'old man' had been treating his corns with caustic. Our first night's rest was by no means perfect. When Baker joined us he was even more worried than the rest of us owing to mysterious noises in one of his drawers. Though if he had investigated he would have found nothing but a tin and a length of string communicating with our room. At the first opportunity we bought large quantities of lavender oil to deal with the insects and had better nights afterwards.

Plan and section of Lamb Lair Cavern, based on surveys by W. McMurtrie (1880) and H.E. Balch (1904) and drawn by JHS

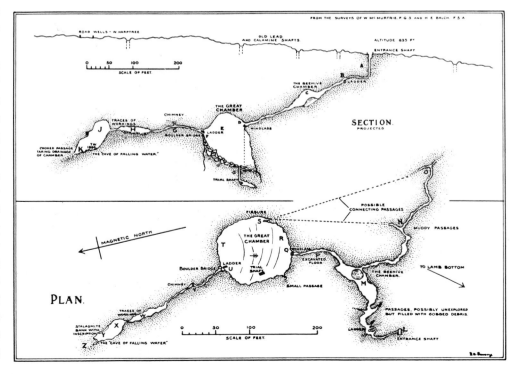

LAMB LAIR 6 September 1913 (Saturday)

Baker and Blake walked, Chandler and self started on bikes at 10.45 a.m. and arrived at Lamb Lair at 11.30, and at 11.45 Barker and another man turned up. Spent a little time sawing a pin and strutting loose stones opposite the little earthen platform 20 ft down. The Bristol men had cleared the shaft well; it was very different from the condition we found it in at our last visit. We anchored a rope ladder at the top and used this part of the way down, changing to the old timber ladder which was in a very bad state. One of the party moved the foot of the bottom ladder, the strut for which had fallen away, thereby loosening much earth and small stuff which rattled down, nearly blocking the hole at the bottom of shaft. There is much mud just about here and one does a creep through a little hole low down into the first natural passage which strikes off horizontally from the vertical shaft. Some of the others cleared away the fall somewhat while one or two of us went on (to the Beehive) along the passage to an S bend midway to the Beehive Chamber. Here one finds a reasonably sound wooden ladder, drops 15–20 ft on this, then continues along a curved passage where there is some rather fine stalagmite on the walls, and at last comes in at the top of the Beehive Chamber with that colossal boss looming up at one's feet. Numerous fallen stalactites were firmly sealed into its crown; I took a view at close quarters and one of the whole chamber, our first had been at the entrance. We had food here and went on down the passage, which was very muddy, to the windlass, which at the time of its erection must have been a very solid and heavy affair. Huge banks firmly anchored to the ground support the windlass over the brink of the drop on cantilevers. Now it was decaying and though much sound wood remains in the cores of the baulks, one can push a penknife in an inch or so with ease and it is difficult to say how safe or unsafe it is. The passage opens but slightly and forms a little grotto; much of the pure white aragonite had been cut through here to get extra depth and width, and many pieces as white as Carrara [marble] were lying about. We dropped shreds of magnesium over the brink to get our first impression of the vast chamber which lies below, the distant walls over opposite could be dimly seen. Baker and I

6 September 1913. Lamb Lair: a party starting down the entrance shaft, Read, Barker, an unidentified person, Chandler, Baker and Blake; half-plate

6 September 1913. Lamb Lair: Blake at the Beehive, the largest known English stalagmite boss; half-plate

6 September 1913. Lamb Lair: Baker starting down the ladder into the Great Chamber (seen beyond the platform), with a safety line over the windlass held by Read. Also shown are Barker (with pipe) and Chandler; half-plate

tossed for honour of first descent, and having lost I got another good plate of him as he disappeared on the rope ladder through a hole in the platform, starting down with much friendly advice and cautions not to fall off or do anything else rash. The safety line, passed *outside* the windlass, was fastened onto him. I followed him and once on the ladder one seemed to be going down and down for an interminable time, another man followed, then Blake and Chandler.

The floor is a chaos of stones and boulders, sloping up from the foot of the ladder at 30°; there is a trial pit in the mud at the bottom. We climbed up the slope to get a good idea of the size of the place, it was immense, a white spot high up and low down marked the head and foot of the ladder, and a little magnesium burnt by the man remaining at the windlass threw beams across the chamber over our heads. Between the lights there was a black void, except when we lighted magnesium and then the further walls receding in the distance were just visible. One starts down the ladder where it hangs close against the wall sloping slightly outwards, then the wall recedes as one reaches a point in the general line of the domed roof, and gradually falls back from the rope ladder which, for the first man anyway, without a steadying hand at the bottom, starts swinging and turning round. The great thing is to keep one's hands on the ropes, not on the rungs, and hug the ladder well up to one's chest, otherwise the feet swing forward from under one. After this one soon loses the sense of having any wall nearby at all, and feels that the ladder just hangs in a great empty black space. At the bottom the wall has receded so far that it is many feet away from the ladder. We had tried one or two Roman Candles in the Great Chamber but these were perhaps damp and the whole place was filled with a dense fog, so that at a short distance one could hardly see each other's candles. The reports we were almost afraid might bring down some rock. There are some fair terraces on the N. side of this chamber where several evaporation tests had been started by the Bristol men, zinc pans with covers held above to shelter from drip.

The way on is through a very muddy winding and low passage where one goes on hands and knees, starting under a natural bridge formed by two or three gigantic fallen boulders at the top of the boulder floor. From this passage several promising looking chimneys go up. We soon arrived at a sort of lobby to the second chamber, 'The Cave of Falling Water', which is entered by a loose slope down of 60° where a rope is useful to help one scramble down. Looking across the top from the entrance which is almost level with the roof, there can be seen a curious bit of wall on the further side, out of reach of anyone, bearing a remarkable resemblance to brickwork. On one's right are some shattered boulders. Barker, another man and myself went down; on a high bank of stalactite running down the right wall right to the floor, and near the floor, is an inscription cut out with the point of a pick, T.W. 1894. Even the white surface fracture from the pick point has not yet been obliterated by new deposit and this is a good example of the slow growth of the stalagmite. I took one half-plate from the lobby above looking across the roof. Twenty feet up from the lower end in the opposite wall is a little mud passage leading on, but this is not a likely way on we think.

We returned to the Great Chamber earlier than expected and the men at the top were away investigating a branch passage which runs out of the Beehive Chamber, ending now in a mud choke, but we think it likely that it works round and downwards to a recess at N. end of Great Chamber where a group of glass jars (evaporation test) now stand. We shouted but there was no response and Barker went up shortly afterwards without the safety line, rather a risky proceeding. We took a photo of Blake on the bottom of the rope ladder with Chandler steadying it. Baker went up, then Blake, 'Tom', Chandler, another man and myself last. The safety rope had twisted round the ladder coming down and I had to make three changes on the way up. The windlass at length loomed up ahead and I was hauled onto the platform with a cheer. We rolled up rope ladder, packed other things and met the other men back in the Beehive Chamber, where fumes from the Roman Candles were detected distinctly, it was thought reaching that point by a different passage. Back to foot of entrance shaft where another deluge of earth was sent down on top of me by Blake. One of the old ladders is overhung and holds back a mass of stuff so that the uprights are like bows, very dangerous. Got onto earth platform near top, hauled all the kit out and finally reached the ground level in darkness, but with bright stars out overhead.

10 September 1913 (Wednesday)

Wookey Hole with EAB who distinguished himself by walking into a 3 ft pool in the first chamber. Dug for an hour or so at the tunnel Balch had started at the foot of the second ladder climb W. series, did not make much progress, then went round W. series. A favourite phrase of EAB's used this holiday and one we pulled his leg over 'I will go on and reconnoitre' (specially if there was any awkward digging going on). In the evening the sun set directly behind Brent Knoll seen from gate left of road just above the Manor Farm and everything was bathed in a golden haze.

CHEDDAR 11 September 1913 (Thursday)

Baker showed me where the Bone Hole was in the little tributary ravine. Looked in at the Long Hole, where soft plastic stalactite lines the wall, and located Priddy Slit which is not a cave but a great fissure in the cliff. Climbed up to the Roman Cave above Gough's and got one or two good photos. The approach is very steep, narrow and winding, and it must have been a very strong point of defence in the old days. One of Baker's exposures he stated he would give a 1/45 second, an unusual sort of shutter to have this speed. Looked in at Gough's Old Cave and Cox's 1913 chamber and returned to Milton by the lower road.

SWILDON'S HOLE 12 September 1913 (Friday)

An easy day. Went through the first water

6 September 1913. Lamb Lair: Blake starting the ascent from the floor of the Great Chamber, being steadied by Chandler; half-plate

12 September 1913. Swildon's Hole: the Pagoda stalagmite and surrounding formations in the Old Grotto; half-plate

rift and tried to take particular note of all the right angle turns before one reaches the head of dry way. The stalactite bridge in the large stalactite grotto seemed very dry and rotten today. Plenty of mud in lower chamber and passage.

On 15 September the party dispersed. It was during this holiday that Baker received a card from some Yorkshire Rambler friends on the Continent, who through going abroad were prevented from joining them on Mendip. The greeting ran: 'From Hearts High in Hartz to Men Deep in Mendip' (i.e. the Harz Mountains in Germany).

There was only one more trip recorded in 1913, to Worlebury Camp near Weston-Super-Mare with John Hassall on 5 October.

WORLEBURY 5 October 1913

With John Hassall, had to think of something new so chose this spot. We cut across the links past two gullies running down N. side of hill, to the flats below. From here we had a splendid view right up the Channel to Portishead with the glasses, we could see Sand Point and the intervening bay, Woodspring, Worle, Wraxall on N. right round to the E. We then dived into the woods and soon came across some of the pit dwellings which are of quite a good size. We failed to mark the E. ramparts, however. After fighting our way through the wood for half a mile or more we struck a path on the N. side and followed this until we could turn sharply to the left across the hill, and this soon brought us to the outer rampart of loose stone and a little further to the inner. The

might of these in places is immense and we came across just one or two spots where (presumably) the original vertical old walling was left. Soon we were right round, walking on its crest, until we were overlooking Weston sands where great crowds were assembled to see the motor racing. Not heeding this we went along the now quite straight line of rampart (S. side) towards the sea where it gives way to the natural defence of the cliff overlooking Burnbeck Island and the Old Pier. We climbed down here and half-way took refuge in a little natural shelter.

Rain was a downpour for some while but we soon escaped down to the road and into a hotel overlooking the sands where we got a good lunch. Weather still very threatening, and we got caught badly when out on

12 September 1913. Refreshment in the New Inn, Priddy, after a trip down Swildon's Hole; left to right, rustic, JHS, Blake, Baker and Chandler; half-plate

the sands watching the racing. It was not long before we picked up the car at the other end and were soon spinning along to Uphill and the mouth of the Axe. This I had not seen for some time and very picturesque and wild it is, tide was naturally out but it is most interesting all round. The ferry is marked with a pole and steps down the steep and muddy banks, while looking out to sea there is the bold cliff of Brean Down on your left and a clump of rocks jutting out of the sand on the right (Blackrock). The river is tidal here and facing about one sees the flats towards Brent, and on the left the bold Uphill hill crowned with tower and old church, where the last remains are to be found of *Via ad axium*, far better known to me 15 miles further inland.

1914–1918

In 1914 Wookey Hole, Its Caves and Cave Dwellers *was finally published and JHS joined the Bristol Naturalists' Society. His membership of this society was interrupted by war-time service, however, and he did not rejoin until 1931. There were only three visits to Mendip recorded in 1914, all very briefly in note form, presumably because JHS was preoccupied with events leading up to the declaration of war on 3 August. He visited Gough's Cave, Cheddar on 31 January, and stayed at Green Ore for the weekend from 27–29 February, when he talked with Balch and walked to Eastwater, Swildon's Hole, depressions near Castle of Comfort, Miles Lot and a promising looking swallet in Island plantation. He returned to Green Ore with Dick Savory for the Easter Holiday from 9 to 15 April.*

10 April 1914 (Good Friday)

Not far in the morning, Eastwater boulders. From 2 p.m. on surveyed stream up to wall. Boulders down to mineral vein very wet, several boulders look bad. Walked across to Swildon's Hole, watercress and sandwiches. Swallet near Weeks' farm house, workings behind.

11 April 1914 (Saturday)

Excavated Island [Plantation] Swallet considerably, good stream going, see well in among small boulders. Signalling afternoon, Pen Hill to Haystack above Island.

There was another expedition which was not recorded in the diary at all, but for which 1914 seems the most likely date. It was to Coral Cave with G. Barker, W. J. Brownsey and E. K. Perdue, all members of the Bristol Spelaeological Research Society (BSRS), and (unlike the previous visit on 26 December 1911) successful photographs were taken.

When war broke out, JHS was posted to the 1st Field Company of the 61st (South Midland) Division of the Royal Engineers as a Second Lieutenant, later rising to be Captain. As a sapper he was responsible for digging and repairing trenches, building dugouts and putting up barbed wire entanglements. His movements are not known, although he was certainly at Ypres, and a description by him of life in the trenches, 'somewhere in Flanders' appeared in the WNHAS Proceedings for 1914. In the same Company were associates from Bristol including at least one from E.W. Savory Ltd. On the back of his identity disc he scratched

22 February or April 1913. Gough's Cave: in the Diamond Chamber with Solomon's Temple above; whole-plate

21 August 1916. A cottage on the Batch, Priddy, and some of the '52 Weeks' (the commonest name in Priddy);
half-plate

KEEP SMILING, and on one occasion, at Voormezeele, he took refuge in a ruined church where he found a broken off cherubim's head painted in gold leaf which he eventually brought home.

On 1 April 1916, JHS was severely wounded when a sniper's bullet ricocheted and hit him in the neck. Remarkably, nothing vital was damaged, but even so, he was kept in hospital in France until late July, and then spent another week in a London hospital in early August before finally arriving home on sick leave. He then spent nearly three weeks at Green Ore, from 16 August to 3 September (when the 1916 diary ends), renewing old friendships and exploring the area as before, but did only one caving trip into Wookey Hole.

17 August 1916 (Thursday)

Went to Hillgrove, much the same. Explored eastwards and came across most interesting line of active swallets and depressions, ten or twelve in all, some of the swallets quite important. Conglomerate boulders exposed at two of these, very interesting as this is N. of Hillgrove Swallet taking a line E. and W. Limestone shows at Hillgrove and on the Masbury Road (quarry). Is conglomerate shown on O.S. map? This is a very good example. This line is quite an important discovery and worth taking up, one in field might repay well a few hours hard work, photos.

21 August 1916 (Monday)

Priddy Fair. Got there about 10.15, things just starting, not quite so many people as usual, no side shows, chiefly horses, ponies and sheep, few cattle. Watched the auctioneer selling sheep. Met farmer Main. Got good photos from E. and S. and a pretty cottage next to tumble down thatched cottage on the Batch belonging to T. Weeks. This is a pretty corner and deserves attention. Old characters still about, many old drovers, great variety of headgear, everything but a topper could be seen. Interesting to watch bargains being struck. A few pens of the real Mendip sheep, very little and khaki. All the village children in their Sunday best, winkle stall! Left about noon, came home and took Green Ore pub with the timber wagons but old Pierce wasn't having any.

28 August 1916 (Monday)

2.30 p.m. started out for Wookey Hole, put in an afternoon 3–6 p.m. alone there. Got a good detail photo of the large active cave pool. Tried one of lower end of second chamber, two of pools between first and second, one of which if it comes out ought to be a topping picture. In many places small patches of gleaming white show where the drip is starting to cover the soot from the petrol. In the pools between first and second chambers I came across several small freshwater shrimps, nearly white.

30 August 1916 (Wednesday)

Stormy first thing. About 11 started to Red Quar. There was a strong stream running from the spring under the wall S. side of

21 August 1916. Timber wagons at the Ne Nimium Inn, Green Ore; half-plate

road and 300 yd E. of Bendall's Lot. This runs down the road for 100 yd then in under the wall again and soaks away in a little marshy swallet, just near the wee triangular plantation. Apparently last night and yesterday's deluge were a bit of a record on Mendip, so HEB says who was at Rookham. All the swallets were engulfing large quantities of water and the springs were full. The above spring always works after rain, at other times being usually quite dry. At Red Quar the 'Pond' spring was running fairly hard and also the main spring. The swallet looks much as it always has. The numerous small springs which act as tributaries to the two main springs were running well and the top-most one was actually under strong pressure, the water welling up into a cone and spurting through my fingers when I pressed my hand on it. All the small springs have had trenches cut. The little swallet in the corner of the field was acting well. I saw young moorhens at the spring and on the pond even though it is so small, and that reminds me that one or two days ago Mr Symes put up a wild goose from the little pond halfway down S. side of Furzewell Hill near the Tor Hole to Green Ore footpath.

I got over the wall and was surprised to find the largest depression is apparently active in wet weather. A large standing pool in the lower (S.) half of the depression 40 ft by 30 ft at least and water standing high over the heads of the ragwort growing there so at deepest it must have been 3 ft 6 in and averaging 2 ft so that at least 2400 cu ft of water was there. In the swallet hole in the N. half a little stream was running in from a spring on N. side. All the springs round the E. side were either wet or just running. A little further on near the Barrow were ten large ponds all round it, some very shallow others 2 ft deep. I walked on down the workings towards the mines and was surprised to find numerous well-defined rakes mostly running S.E. to N.W. (most on Mendip have an E. and W. direction), but there were no good exposures of rock face. Down on to the road, the Wheelpit swallet was dry, the big one running a little but was dry a week ago. Back across the workings taking a more N. line over the big round barrow. Here are some really good rakes (E. and W.) with splendid conglomerate exposures like the limestone exposures at Charterhouse but on a smaller scale. Interesting in that the Dolomitic conglomerate was far disintegrated, the large round pebbles actually falling out in places and in others it could be broken. A heap of exposed excavated earth near the little shed alongside the cultivated patch further E. gave some good specimens of a very interesting crystal which HEB believes to be barita. Very heavy and at first I thought it lead, it was easily broken. There were pebbles in it and in some the rain had washed out the intervening grains. Crystal reddish and long, something like asbestos, at different angles. Also picked up a highly-polished limestone pebble at same place, cracked and recemented, probably owing to a movement in the conglomerate from which it must have come. Home to lunch.

In afternoon met HEB at Wookey Hole where he was taking over a party. Reconstructed a lias hearth at entrance, saw a live frog in second chamber, out at 4.30. Walked with him to Rookham where I had tea.

3 September 1916 (Sunday)

Met Balch and Barnes and his brother at Red Quar at 10.30 and went over to look at the depressions. Water quite gone from the pool in large one, the swallet, which is to be called 'Red Quar West', with just a little running into the hole. HEB thinks that this is a barrow here all right. Went over to the workings which are very sharply divided by the old earth bank which was either a contemporary boundary or else later and the N. part been levelled, former more probable. In the depressions through which the wall runs we found some fine blocks of silicious shore lias with very numerous impressions of pecten [scallop] and less of other shells. There being no lime in this rock the shells themselves are not preserved but disappear. The same stuff is to be found on the lip of Wurt Pit, it marks the shores of a lias sea rich in silica round a Mendip isle.

Cycled from here to the quarries at Tor Hole which might pay further investigation. It is very interesting to find conglomerate and well defined limestone slabs in the same quarry (the middle one), and shows that about here the conglomerate is but a thin layer on the limestone. Tor Hole valley is presumably superficial.

Cycled on to Greg's pit which was much enjoyed. Seems open to question as to whether this is superficial or not as the presence of tufa (containing the miners' charcoal) in big quantities seems to show that a stream once ran down here and this is

so according to old James Payne who says he remembers it.

Although this was the last entry for 1916, one of JHS's albums contains photographs taken by him in Cheddar Gorge and dated 12 October 1916. Eventually, however, he rejoined his Company.

War ended on 11 November 1918, but JHS's only diary entries that year were three before Armistice Day, for 7–9 September, recording part of a week's stay at Vicar's Close in Wells. Presumably his Company was sent home early or he was on leave again.

7 September 1918 (Saturday)

Did all Wookey Hole except beyond the Grill with HEB, Capt. Hincks and Maj. MacGillicuddy.

8 September 1918 (Sunday)

Ebbor in afternoon with HEB, saw the cave mouths on E. side above ravine and on E. side just below the ravine. Both have been worked at with good results, remains human and animal. B. told me of old mining claim Mid. Horrington Hill, owner now Hawkins, only remaining relic of its kind. White Hairbell blooming between Rookham and Ebbor. Pen Hill gold with fine orange gorse, second flowering. Very weird old ash N.W. corner of square wood S. slope of Pen. Green Ore after tea. A. Symes attacked by big stoat, came into kitchen hanging onto neck of game hen, climbed onto chair and table, finally killed in grate. B. told me of a

12 October 1916. A bit of old Cheddar, the Lion Rock and early morning mists hanging on the cliffs of the gorge; whole-plate

colourless rainbow over Mendip, remarked in Bristol papers of same date. Coast visible down to [Countisbury] Foreland.

9 September 1918 (Monday)

Ebbor morning. Green Ore afternoon and evening. Wind high, storms very bad, seen approaching from Channel. Caught in bad storm at Red Quar, sheltered in the Ball's cottage there. Pulled a good bit of stuff out of swallet, this is getting enlarged. Green Ore wood and Bendall's Lot nearly all gone [cut down during the war]. Mrs Webb tells me her father seventy years ago penetrated beyond third chamber Wookey Hole with party, used boat, ½ lb of dips [candles] used on journey in and same amount outwards. Dog released at furthest point reached, came out at Cheddar!

JHS also had an unrecorded trip down Swildon's Hole in September, with Balch, Baker and others. They studied erratic stalactites in the Long Dry Way, and JHS made a series of ink drawings of these 'from sketches made on the spot' which were included in the MNRC Annual Report in the WNHAS Proceedings for 1918.

September 1918. Pen drawing by JHS from a sketch made on the spot of the Imp, an erratic group (now destroyed) in Swildon's Hole Long Dry Way

THE IMP.

9 June 1919. Swildon's Hole: Brownsey in the passage between the Old Grotto and lower water chamber; half-plate

1919–1920

In 1919 JHS renewed his visits to Mendip much as before, except that very little caving was done, and several of the visits that are represented by dated photographs went unrecorded in his diary; also some diary entries are out of sequence, indicating that they were written after some delay. Possibly his enthusiasm for caving and for upkeep of the diary were beginning to wane. Only three of the twenty-six entries for the year record trips into caves, but one other expedition, to Swildon's Hole on 9 June, can be identified from photographs in one of his albums.

Some caving in 1919 was done with members of the newly formed University of Bristol Spelaeological Society, of which JHS was a committee member. The UBSS, which has always had a core of non-student members, was inaugurated on 19 March 1919 and superseded the BSRS, which had been formed in 1912 but disbanded in 1914 because of the war. There seems to have been a degree of rivalry between MNRC and UBSS, and MNRC is reputed to have regarded most of Mendip as their territory with the exception of the Burrington area where UBSS was based. As a gesture of goodwill, however, the two societies did hold a few joint expeditions, by invitation, and the Swildon's Hole trip on 9 June, for example, was specifically to show UBSS members the cave. JHS may have been the only one then who was a member of both societies.

The first entry for 1919 is 1 March, when JHS went to Winscombe and then walked up and over Crook's Peak to Compton Bishop and Axbridge. The following weekend he stayed at Weston-super-Mare with friends and on 29 March he went to Winscombe again. A week later, on 5 April, he had his first outing with UBSS (founder) members, Lionel (Leo) Palmer, Reginald Read, Jack Brownsey and (?) Edwards.

5 April 1919 (Saturday)

Motorbiked to Burrington. Met Palmer at P.O., took up two 30 ft and one 60 ft rope and reached Goatchurch at 11 a.m. Joined by Read, Brownsey and Edwards at 11.30. Started in at noon and got out at 3.30. The 'Tunnel' near the bottom rather tough, 40 ft horizontal, very smooth and round just fitting the body, with arms forward one cannot change position till through the further end [this is now called the 'Drainpipe']. Read's Chamber was interesting. Returned to entrance via Coal Chute, reached by a turning off the main line on return journey, on right just above first

Boulder Chamber. Saw one lesser horseshoe bat in the Chute.

JHS's Easter holiday started after work on Thursday 17 April, when he motor-cycled out from Park Row to Burrington. As well as his usual half-plate camera, the Goerz Ans-chutz, he had with him for the first time an Ensignette film camera, which took 2 in by 3 in negatives and which he used only for photographs above ground. On Good Friday 18 April, he went by motorbike to Charterhouse and used the Ensignette to take photographs outside and inside the new little church there. He went to Green Ore for lunch and then returned to Burrington. After supper he 'went up and charted the mine field above the village, very extensive all round Hill gardens and some well-defined rakes, close together, running parallel, E. and W., up to Ellick farm. Saw my first swallow of the year.' On 19 April, the first field day of the UBSS, JHS joined a crowd of members in the afternoon for a trip down Goatchurch, followed by tea at Mrs Cox's (Burrington).

On Easter Sunday, 20 April, JHS went to the early and morning services in Burrington church and to Beacon Batch to count barrows in the afternoon. He had tea at Langford Court and then continued charting the mine workings above Burrington on a 6-in map. On 21 April, he went by motorbike to Wurt Pit near E. Harptree to meet 'young Tucker, who did not turn up' (Tucker's farm was S. of Wurt Pit). 'Found out afterwards that he had strained himself blowing a set of moorhen's eggs and was not fit. I gave him an hour, then went over and took a photo of Wurt Pit and talked to a wood cutter who had taken off

some time before two fingers clean with his own hedging hook.' On the last day of his holiday, 22 April, he was shown round the trout hatchery at Ubley Mill by Donald Carr, fishing warden and naturalist at nearby Blag-don Lake. JHS spent the rest of the day, with the Goerz Anschutz and binoculars, watching birds at the E. end of Blagdon Lake.

Further trips during May and June are evident from dated photographs. At Whit-suntide (8–10 June) he stayed with MNRC members E. A. Baker and J. A. Bonner at Ernest Speed's house next to Priddy Green. They explored Priddy and Cheddar Gorge on the 8th, took a party of UBSS members down Swildon's Hole on the 9th, fired a charge at Plantation Swallet at Priddy Mines, and went to Eastwater farm and Green Ore on the 10th.

On Saturday 5 July JHS went to Wookey Hole with Bonner and E. L. Bird and did the main series and whole of the W. series through Purgatory to the Terminal Cham-ber. There then followed two walking weekends with his friends the Sainsburys, who had one house in Weston and another in Winscombe, on the second of which they went to Uphill where they saw the quarry and remains of the old bone cave.

For his main August holiday JHS had planned a 'cave hunting venture' in Ireland, but this had to be cancelled, so instead he walked along the Somerset coast from Countisbury Foreland back to Bristol. The walk took ten days and he made a hand-written record of it in an attractive leather-bound book, illustrated with photographs taken with the Ensignette. Soon after this, the family moved house to The Chantry in

9 June 1919. Swildon's Hole: in the lower water chamber, a visit of some of the University of Bristol Spelaeological Society, left to right, Gadd, Balch, Bird, Sinnock, unidentified, Barnes, Brownsey, Read, Edwards, Peet, Creecy, unidentified, Troup; half-plate

Church Road, Abbots Leigh, a short way from Bristol on the Somerset side of the Avon. The second part of JHS's holiday was spent with the Symes at Green Ore from 16–22 August.

17 August 1919 (Sunday)

Walked round Green Ore wood with Mr Symes, every tree down now but the two hardly tried stumps by road used for derrick. Worked up to Long Belt and found workings extended up and past this a little northwards, thus making this area of workings broader than I had thought. Saw some very good rakes in Long Belt, like those at Charterhouse but smaller. Later in morning went to Hillgrove. Much collapse, big boulders fallen in and earthen arch as I last saw it, fallen away altogether. Hopeless to try anything here by myself. Everything points to the fact that we are on the right line. Tackle and party of three or four required. Ought not to take a great deal of time to get in. Big upright boulder which used to be on left of entrance now standing up on its own, poised rather badly, will have to be cracked and removed.

18 August 1919 (Monday)

Set out to explore fields and woods from Green Ore farm to Stock Hill. Many fields show signs of levelling but one is apt to confuse this with small natural depressions such as on all the Hillgrove fields. There seems to be no doubt that hereabouts was one of the biggest continuous mining areas. Worked up through Golden Batch, ash plantation and Tower Hill wood, lime kiln in heart of this wood absolutely covered over with wild strawberries. Then Sandbatch E. of nursery, pool in Bendall's Lot, new trees coming on well. Through here on to Stock Hill, unlevelled patch of workings, then big levelled field W. to next wall. Watched countless swarms of rabbits on the big mine field (Stock Hill), down wall to Red Quar, much earth washed in covering up my previous opening. Across to Tor Hole ridge and Rodney Pits plantation, now nearly all down, Furzewell Hill plantation, then down the hill when I heard Baker with the Taxi whistle some distance off. Down Rodney Pits, met Mr Symes then Baker and walked back to lunch.

Weather very doubtful, Baker went off towards Harptree, I fetched long ladder with Mr Symes and trimmed as much as I could of the ivy round [Green Ore] Mission chimney, top four courses in a very bad way, several bricks fell off. After tea cycled over to Holcombe with I.S. [Symes ?] by Binegar Lane and Gurney Slade, fine view of valley eastwards, covered in a rainy haze, raining hard, arrived very wet. Visited Mr Wickham, author of *Spade and Terrier* and saw his Mendip Map. He told me he had found a reference in a book dealing with Egyptian archaeology on a secondary burial in the Neolithic period, when bones after the flesh had gone (perhaps by scraping) were then collected together and arranged side by side (and not buried as a perfect skeleton in human form) and buried finally. He says that it was perfectly evident that the bones he found in the Holcombe Longbarrow were thus arranged.

9 June 1919. Swildon's Hole: in the chamber below the Imp, Long Dry Way; half-plate

Found I.S. and proceeded about a mile to Holcombe Old Church down in the valley, only used now for burials in the graveyard. Funerals have to go through a very rough farmyard, no road to church, no services there now. Fine Norman arch over S. porch and interesting early Gothic (?) crooked chancel arch, all woodwork inside painted white, old box pews (of oak?), some with seats, round three sides. Crazy old pulpit and clerk's desk, toy gallery over Norman (?) arch at W. end also very crazy. This and the fact that the church is set down amongst trees right away from anywhere makes it a very eerie spot. Grave mounds are all coffin-shaped, the village sexton's fancy I suppose! Captain Scott's (Antarctic man) people are buried behind the church. Most of the windows are broken.

We had been in the church some 10 minutes and were standing near the W. end when suddenly I noticed what appeared to be a deep and regular breathing coming from over our heads. I called the others' attention to it, with natural results. Occasionally I thought I could hear the inspiration as well as the expiration, it sounded rather forced like someone in a bad way. A pair of boots on the stairs of the little gallery made things more mysterious, though these were dry and dusty. There was a terrible smell too. After some discussion I fetched a candle (there are about five single candlesticks in the church besides those at the altar), lit it and, undoing the hasp, which by the way was fastened, I ventured up the smallest and fustiest spiral stone staircase I'd ever seen. A turn or two brought me to the first floor of the tower, covered in filth and with oak beams carrying two small bells. There was no sign of anything or anybody and I could see nothing whatever up above me. The noise had stopped and I couldn't see any birds, bats or rats about, so I came down and it started again. We gave it up, went round outside, but could see that there was no other way into the tower but the little staircase inside. I was leading as we went out through the porch, but I was pushed aside as one of the girls rushed out first with a polite 'excuse me'! By this time it was nearly dark. They told me the tale of a man who, for a wager, said he would dig a grave at night in this churchyard, but who fled in terror soon after he had started. I.S. was much too wet already to return to Green Ore and it was still pouring, so after a little cocoa at Mrs ?, I came home by myself, found the road most confusing, got in at 10 p.m. and found them getting anxious. The sexton's tools, grubbing axe, spade etc. in the church did not make things more cheerful.

20 August 1919 (Wednesday)

Rained hard all the morning without stopping. 2.30 p.m. at Burnt Wood (now nearly all down) as arranged with Baker who sent messenger saying he was going to Wookey Hole. I declined and stuck to my original programme, Holcombe by same road as on Monday. Took three or four interiors of church and entrance arch then thoroughly explored tower to try and find the gent in the belfry, more light today. On first floor, in fact all over the inside of tower was a mass of owl's pellets, dead moles, parts of rats and owl's feathers; this accounted for the smell! Climbed up above the bells but could see no sign of any living thing, the birds were not at home. Evidently the noise was due to owls. Symes tells me he has heard them make the same sort of 'breathing' noise up in the trees.

Returned key, cycled on down through Edford, tea, and up to Stoke Lane, hunted out the swallet, downstream from the mill, a very picturesque spot. Boulders overgrown with trees, only a trickle running down today and entrance looks fairly easy. EAB [Baker] says there is a good rising further down the valley. A fine creeper covered the church and a very fine pub, old style, the name is now changed but used to be 'The Treasure of Theophilus' (EAB). Other fine old cottages and houses unspoilt by the collieries which have crept out in all directions here. On to Long Cross mentioned in 'Mendippe Mappe', no sign of cross now.

21 August 1919 (Thursday)

Priddy Fair. Got along there about 11 a.m., many people on all the roads going there, a bigger crowd than usual, some very interesting real old English characters out today, a good bright day for it. Four or five caravan loads of gypsies, 'travellers' they call themselves, including the 'Bowers', a fat policeman, Old Moore [a seller of Old Moore's Almanac], three Jews giving away watches, rings and bracelets! Three or four real old drovers and many real old farmers. The marquee was up and amusements such as coconut shies, hitting the bell and hoopla soon began to arrive. A fried fish stall on

wheels from Wells, winkle stalls, lemonade stalls. Old Moore, seventy-one years old, was one from Shepton who sold many gross during the year and did something in tinware in his spare time. Horses of all sorts and many sheep but few cattle.

The following weekend JHS stayed again at Winscombe, as can be ascertained from photographs taken thereabouts and dated 26–28 August. This was his last known visit to the Mendips that year.

In 1919, therefore, there appears to have been more social activity and greater interest in natural history. There may also have been increased interest in churches, possibly related to JHS's experiences in the war; he was a regular churchgoer throughout his life and later became involved actively with the Moral Re-Armament movement.

*There also appears to have been little or no contact with Balch, apart from the joint expedition down Swildon's Hole on 9 June. According to William Stanton's biography of Herbert Balch (*Pioneer Under the Mendips*, Wessex Cave Club, 1969), 'In the year after the war ended, Balch reached the age of 50. Although a major caving triumph still lay ahead of him, he devoted only a small part of his time to the sport. His love of archaeology was more than ever foremost, leading him to the hills and especially the ploughed fields where, as his daughter Margaret recalled, his whole family would form a line, arms-length apart, and spend afternoons walking systematically back and forth searching for flints.' Much of JHS's caving activity in the past had clearly stemmed*

21 August 1919. Priddy Fair, a seller of Old Moore's Almanack; from 3 in × 2 in film negative

directly from Balch's inspiration and leadership, so perhaps a decline in Balch's caving can account at least partly for the apparent changes in JHS's interests and for his new affiliation with the UBSS.

There are no diary entries at all for 1920, but from photograph captions it can be seen that JHS had at least one caving trip, down Eastwater Cavern on Whit Monday 24 May with Balch, E. Bird and Oxenham, and did some excavating at Plantation Swallet (date unknown). There were also trips to the Exmoor region in January and August. The most likely reason for reduced activity on Mendip was that JHS was courting 'the girl next door' (literally) in Abbots Leigh, Doris Lane. They were married in November 1920, and lived in a flat in the same house as her parents (Swallowfield) until their own home was built in 1923.

1921

1921 marked the end of JHS's upkeep of his Mendip diary, but not of his caving activity, which continued sporadically for a few more years. There were twenty-six entries for the year, most of which were during his summer holiday, and eight of which record cave exploration. As well as renewed excavation at Hillgrove Swallet and at Ebbor, there were several expeditions down Swildon's Hole. This was because the exceptionally dry summer greatly reduced the water flowing over the 40 ft pot there which separates the upper and lower series. Up to this point the pot had been passed only two or three times, and it presented a very real barrier to progress because the approach to it through the tight water rift was liable to flood, and because of the difficulty of descending a rope ladder suspended in the middle of a waterfall with only a candle for illumination. The dry weather of 1921 allowed work in the water rift to improve the approach, and a metal chute to be fitted at the top of the drop for diverting the water.

The first five diary entries are merely notes on a scrap of paper, presumably intended to be written up in more detail. The first was for 25 May, when JHS and other UBSS members went by charabanc to their club hut at Burrington for a picnic lunch attended by guests from the university staff. These included Professor Sollas, who formally opened the Society's new 'Swimming Bath', built of bricks in the nearby Bath Swallet depression. The party also visited the entrances of Keltic Cavern and Aveline's Hole. The other notes refer to the weekend 15–18 July, when JHS and Doris Savory, who was now pregnant, stayed with a Dr Wood at Yatton on Friday the 15th, and with the Sainsburys at Winscombe on the 16th and 17th. They went to Shipham, Rowberrow Bottom, Keltic Cavern and the UBSS hut on the 16th, Winterhead Hill on the 17th, and returned home on the 18th.

JHS's summer holiday lasted from Saturday 30 July to Monday 14 August and was spent staying first with the Hillards at Eastwater farm (who had replaced Farmer Loxton) and then with the Symes at Green Ore.

EASTWATER FARM 30 July 1921 (Saturday)

Had fixed up a fortnight's Mendip holiday with Mrs Hillard, having several things in view, chief amongst them the big attack on Swildon's and a continuation of digging with Balch at the promising Bone Hole above the

13 August 1921. Swildon's Hole: a party in the Old Grotto, left to right, (sitting) H.E. Balch, Reg Balch,
Tratman, Arthur Main, (standing) unidentified, Ayerst, Revd Quinn, Mrs Quinn, Quinn junior, Ayerst, (front)
Higgins, Simmons, Holly; half-plate

narrows at Ebbor. Had sent on previously a sack of ropes, a new *narrow* 40 ft rope ladder just made by Tench of Broad Quay [Bristol] and various small tools, heavy (10lb) hammer etc., also a roll including a 'muffler' for the 40 ft waterfall described hereafter and a pipe and container for the proposed charge in the water rift at Swildon's. These were sent up from Wells to Eastwater by Balch on Saturday night.

Started on motorbike with a heavy cargo of kit, cameras and explosive, and reached Eastwater at about 3 p.m. As arranged, I walked over to Rookham across the fields, taking Eastwater swallet where the valley was bone dry, to talk things over with Balch. His brother Reg was also there. Had tea and was just returning when Bird and his brother rolled up, just out of Swildon's Hole, where over knee deep in mud they had been attempting with Trapnell and Crook to enlarge the under passage below the stalagmite bridge in water rift using my 10lb hammer for the purpose. It is, however, steel like in hardness and very little progress had been made.

Mrs Hillard told me of a man, Barton, who had stopped with them a month before and had done remarkable things on his own in Eastwater and Swildon's, in one case going into Eastwater at 10.30 a.m. and getting out at 4.30 a.m. next day. It was rumoured that Farmer Weeks had heard him moving in the boulders at 10.30 at night, and Barton himself afterwards declared he had just missed a fall of clay, but it was probably neither of these that Weeks heard, probably the scrabbling of rabbits. Balch had also refer-

red to him and said it was possible he would turn up without notice for Monday's jaunt and sure enough he did. I had turned in and was reading when a car from Wells rolled up quite unexpected, he came in. He knocked me up and sat on my bed for half an hour while a room was being got ready for him!

31 July 1921 (Sunday)

Balch came over this morning and we held an inspection of gear, then proceeded to fill a pipe I had brought down with gelignite. This consisted of a piece of boiler tube 4 ft long and $1\frac{1}{4}$ in internal diameter, a point welded on one end and a collar on the other (Gibson 7/6), inside this fitted closely a tin cylinder closed at one end (Ham 3/-). There was also an iron plug with a collar round it for driving the tube without burring over the mouth, thereby preventing the final insertion of the cylinder after positioning. We filled the cylinder with gelignite (5 lb packet 12/6, Chas. H. Britton, East St, Bedminster), 100 per cent stronger than that bought last year. The cartridges were uncovered and fitted in two abreast, each pair rammed home carefully with a rake handle, making certain of contact. Soon we had it full to the mouth and putting it in the pipe took it, carefully padded at each end, down to Swildon's Hole, putting it with sundry ropes and hammers just inside the grating. Balch went back to Rookham, and Barton and I lunched.

In the afternoon I laced $1\frac{1}{2}$-in ropes through the 'muffler' which was nothing more than a series of sacks cut open and strongly stitched together with spreaders at intervals. This was about 25 ft long and could be added to, the idea being that should the 40 ft waterfall tomorrow or any other time be impassable, this could be let down over the stream and duly anchored with the rope ladder over this again. The idea was that the sacking kept out flat by the spreaders would come between the climber on the rope and the stream, and would divert most of the stream water probably and the bad splash from the shoulder over the under cut certainly. This, even should the climber be inclined to swing under the direct fall. Two ropes were threaded through from stretcher to stretcher to support sacking when saturated and also to strengthen it should anyone grab it or need its support. The two stretchers which I estimated would come at the angle (from the gulley to the vertical) in the waterfall were made stronger than the rest to take the weight of man and ladder. A short saw of mine was also to be taken down to adjust the length of the stretchers in the gulley, the others below of course being the full width of the sacking. At 4 p.m. I motorbiked to Green Ore where they had a house full of people. Had tea in the kitchen with G. and Mr S., walked round after and went to service at the Mission, returning to Eastwater immediately afterwards. Took a 5-in surveyor's aneroid I had hired from Husbands (with several more ropes, camera etc.) to put in the cave to adjust itself to the damp atmosphere during the night. These two journeys made the carting from the farm much lighter the following morning.

SWILDON'S HOLE 1 August 1921 (Monday)

Up betimes and into good old caving kit. Made final adjustments to small gear and remaining packets. Balch came along at 8.30 a.m. and we left instructions for the remainder of kit to be brought on. Then he, Barton, Eric and Gordon Bird and I set out across the fields, the advance party of a determined attack, the most serious for many years on Swildon's Hole. We took down hammers, pipe, camera, sticks, aneroid (which by the way had a nasty spill going down the first inclined rift) and were well on the way by 8.45 a.m. As the last man cleared the entrance, signs were heard of the arrival of the next reinforcement.

From here may be read Balch's report written the next morning (in bed) on the day's doings and the great success that crowned our efforts, annotated by myself, a record put to paper while quite fresh in his mind and my own.

Both Mr and Mrs Hillard kindly turned out and raised a supper of cold chicken and hot tea, quantities of the latter. This was about 3.20 a.m. and after yarning a bit Barton and I finally rolled into bed at 4.30. As a result of the work put in on the water rift and the appearance of the wall behind the 40 ft waterfall, Balch's and my ideas were changed regarding the false floor and lower outlet theory. The pipe, hammer and bar were left there, pending further discussion and decision, but in the end it was decided to use them at Hillgrove instead.

A description of the discoveries in Swildon's Hole in 1921 formed the main part of Balch's

John Hassall's drawing, from a sketch by JHS, of the descent of the 40 ft fall in Swildon's Hole during the drought

12 November 1921. Swildon's Hole: looking up the White Way in Barnes' Loop; whole-plate

MNRC Annual Report *for that year, which was illustrated with JHS's photographs and published in the WNHAS* Proceedings. *The discoveries were made on two expeditions beyond the 40 ft drop into the lower series, on 1 August and 12 November. There was, however, another expedition on 21 July, not recorded in the Report, when a small party led by Baker passed the 40 ft and 20 ft drops into previously unexplored passageway and left a cairn at their furthest point reached, just beyond the Double Pots. According to* The History of Mendip Caving *(Peter Johnson, 1967), this expedition was planned in secret and Balch never forgave Baker for his failure to inform the MNRC of his intentions. This was why it was omitted from the Report. On 1 August JHS took photographs in the passage between the 40 ft and 20 ft drops, and the party continued past Baker's Cairn to explore the streamway as far as its eventual termination at what was later called Sump 1. A group consisting of Ernest Barnes, Reg Balch and JHS, who were surveying behind the leading party, discovered the spectacular high level oxbow named Barnes' Loop, after the first man to enter it, with its beautiful White Way. In his Report, Balch describes it thus:*

Barnes' Loop stands unrivalled in its pure whiteness and beauty. Its floor is of the whiteness of Carrara marble and at every step it has a pool of perfect pureness lined throughout and surrounded by crystals, which flash and sparkle with every movement of the lamps. The whole mass has come down from a tributary cave which is visible but has never yet been climbed. The roof and walls are wonderful, and the accumulated crystals form little bays, promontories and islands in the lovely pools. The pendant stalactites no thicker than a blacklead pencil hang in countless numbers down the walls. Where a big pool bars the way, one passed with difficulty to reach a little portal which gave access to the second part of the loop. Here a tower-like pile of stalagmite reaches nearly to the roof and is surmounted by a cap of strange square form. The descent to the lower channel is nearly vertical and somewhat dangerous.

On 2 August, JHS and Barton retrieved ropes and rope ladders from the cave entrance and from Main's farm at Priddy and brought them back to Eastwater farm for drying. In the afternoon they went to Hillgrove and then Rookham to discuss the report with Balch.

3 August 1921 (Wednesday)

Walked round a few of the swallets with Barton in the morning. Plantation Swallet, which looked a lot more promising than when I last left it. Someone had been working there and cleared round the then final boulder in the floor showing its dimensions, this proved afterwards to be Balch. Then on to the minery round the ponds to the Wheel Pit and Road Swallets. Here we parted company, Barton for the Wells bus and I back to lunch.

Had arranged to meet Balch in Ebbor at 1 p.m. I got there late but it was 3 p.m. before he turned up with his brother. The hole I found was called 'Savory's Hole' from the fact that it was I who moved the first stones years ago and squirming in was photographed looking out by Balch [3.9.11]. It had been worked in in 1916 and last year and had now quite a large and roomy entrance going down steeply and extending both sides with a hole in the floor, permitting standing up. A rift tapering up to nothing runs up at the back of the present chamber, its whole width for 12–15 ft in many places having a covering of stalagmite. The hole is situated on the W. side of gorge not 5 yd back from path about 100 yd above the wooden fence across the path, which one has to climb about the same distance again above the Narrows. For some time I could not locate it being too far down gorge but looked at other shelters, that on the W. immediately below Narrows and another high up on the E. some little way further down again. This, however, proved to be only a fissure and not accessible. Balch's spring in the Narrows was dry. On returning upwards once more Balch answered my cooee and his brother joined us shortly afterwards. He had found in previous years portions of five different human jaws, one or more with perfect teeth and one typifying a man of 5 ft 10 in. We dug the sides [of Savory's Hole] till 8 p.m. and found a few fragments, human amongst them, but results were poor.

On 4 August, JHS spent the whole day digging in Savory's Hole at Ebbor with the two Balch brothers. They 'found about half a dozen [bone] fragments but for the most part extremely barren . . . towards the corner we struck that angular water born gravel which had been crossed at other points during the digging.'

5 August 1921 (Friday)

Spent morning winding up ropes and gear and packing same. Barton proposed visiting Eastwater boulders with his father (in his only suit) and the scoutmaster and a few boys in camp now in the mineries. On the spot by 11, only to find that the key was not forthcoming from the wife of Farmer Weeks. However, he and his father proceeded to the Plantation Swallet and moved up many of the stones lying in the stream bed moved from the inner end by myself some time ago with the aid of gelignite [10.6.19]. On his return he reported it about ready for 'getting in', I was sceptical. I lunched at 1 p.m. and set forth for Green Ore with great satisfaction with a full load in the sidecar, looking forward to the comfort I knew I should find there. The Eastwater billet was decidedly rough. Got there at 3, and visited Hillgrove where it is now proposed to fire the pipe charge. Found it had filled up a very great deal in last few years with leaves, earth, mud, etc., and that more boulders had fallen from the bank over the hole. It was impossible to see how they lay owing to accumulated rubbish, and a day or so must certainly be put in here clearing before the pipe can be fired to really good effect. It is however just the thing that is wanted.

WOOKEY HOLE 6 August 1921 (Saturday)

Commander Willes and Dr Williams came down by car from Bristol and arrived about noon, and Hugh Lane brought down by his sister a little later. After lunch, up into the Wookey Hole gorge where there was very little water coming out, then picked up ladder and gear at the farm and went into cave. Did main series, then west. Willes just got through Purgatory but Williams stuck very badly two-thirds way through and with much trouble backed out. Hugh did not attempt it after this demonstration. Found it easier than usual myself. Up into east series, Spur and Wedge, Suspended Boulders, Conglomerate Ceiling and up to the top, dropping through hole in floor and coming out at fissure above doorway. In for about three hours, back to Mrs Spry's to tea. Balch came into W. series and spoke to us but went out to explore the fissure above the sluice with his brother, one that had not been examined previous to a visit by Bird a little earlier. Much evidence of badgers and an entry possible with digging. Saw Balch after tea and examined Troup's first sketch plan and section of the new parts of Swildon's Hole done last Monday, a very satisfactory result which makes the survey of S.H. nearly complete (to be published in the next report). Saw Willes and Williams off and then brought Hugh up to Green Ore for Sunday.

On 7 August, JHS visited Hillgrove with Hugh Lane and Balch for a 'preliminary examination'. Later he went with Lane to Plantation Swallet, Cheddar and Eastwater cave entrance.

HILLGROVE 8 August 1921 (Monday)

Hugh returned to Bristol by 8.14 a.m. bus

from Green Ore. I put in whole day at Hillgrove with pick, shovel and bar, just returning for lunch. Constructed new dam with angle iron and timber above old one and cleared out 4–5 ft of leaves, earth and mud, going down deepest in the old pit in front of upright square boulder on the left till I reached a solid bottom. I could not penetrate with bar anywhere, same difficulty as previously, a doubt as to the real way on. My work today, however, made things much clearer and it is really quite a deep hole now.

The next day, 9 August, JHS 'visited Rodney Pits and Rookery Farm with 5 in × 4 in camera [a size commonly used for Press photography], getting some detail photos of the workings and washing places'. Doris, Frances and Mortimer Savory came by car for the afternoon and they all walked to Pen Hill and Hillgrove.

SWILDON'S HOLE 10 August 1921 (Wednesday)

Pouring rain. Went to Main's barn at Priddy at 10.30 a.m. and waited nearly an hour when Reg Balch came over from Swildon's to say he and HEB had arrived there expecting me. We were going down for the explosive pipe, just a quick journey, and soon got down by the short dry way. RB and I went right through to the 40 ft fall and found a little water going. We wanted to inspect it to decide as to the best sort of chute to have and the best means of fixing it. HEB's latest idea, which promised to be very sound, was to fix a large diameter metal chute in the gully where water runs out of the first little pot below anchorage, to carry all the water in normal times out over the heads of men on the ladder and to let it fall on the further side of the big pot, thereby allowing passage down the rope ladder in all times of normal flow. The gully is admirable for making a cement joint and RB and I, sitting on the big stalagmite covered boss, decided that 6 ft of galvanised metal pipe (not merely curled up but made as a pipe) of about 5 or 6 in diameter would be most satisfactory, supported from anchorages above by stout galvanised wire. If this chute was directed roughly along the left wall, it would be in a direction that would clear all projections ahead and allow for a clear fall. HEB was working all this time at the water passage through the stalagmite dam in water rift with a geological hammer, and enlarged it considerably. We cleared a runway for the water over the pebble dam up to the 40 ft anchorage column, and with just a trifle of work Balch at once reported the water in the passage lowered very perceptibly, the pebbles put in on 1 August again rising above the surface of mud and water, so that with a larger party in view next Saturday it promised for making this passage roomier and drier. The stalactite above it is exceedingly tough for cutting away and this goes very slowly. We got back to the lower water chamber again and, leaving bars and hammer, brought the pipe out by short dry way.

RB and family were now at Eastwater farm so they took pipe over there while I went back to Main's for motorbike and cycled round and picked it up, together with my sack of ropes already dried and packed. Rain still coming down. Back to Green Ore for lunch. RB came along about 4 p.m., having walked owing to breakdown, and we took pipe and bar over to Hillgrove to get rid of it. Fired a first charge of about ten cartridges, which being untamped had absolutely no effect, then the pipe, which we got in for three-quarters of its length behind the head of the long sloping boulder low down on right of the swallet. It only blew off the top 6 in or so of tin container. It was pouring harder than ever and the hole was exceedingly wet, slimy and muddy, so we buried the remainder of pipe in a rabbit hole *pro tem* and each hied homewards. It was a great disappointment after all my trouble that pipe charge failed. I am sure there was no air lock and contact was good, but it was probably too long a charge for its diameter.

BURRINGTON 11 August 1921 (Thursday)

Got camera etc. in trim and met HEB at Eastwater farm at 11 a.m. Took one Bristol rope ladder in side car, one on carrier and started for Burrington via Hunters Lodge and Castle of Comfort. Tratman was in village buying stores but was soon back. We then went over to Rowberrow Cavern situated high up on the shoulder between the two gullies that join in the valley below Rowberrow Warren. We climbed up to the cave where a big amount of excavation had already been done with good vertical faces for working on inside and a broad trench cut at 4–5 ft lower level out to tip. Got a general view of the entrance and tried another of the working faces, former poor and latter a failure. This cave is situated in Dolomitic conglomerate which filled the main valley here and was a cave of *outlet* when floor of old valley was much higher. Returned to Keltic [now Read's] Cavern and Balch went off for wurts [whortleberries] while Tratman and I went down for photography. An up view of main chamber from W. end lighted from four points, foreground proved under-exposed, two of 'the grotto' from each end, the boulder bridge and the group of erratics opposite foot of slide. Out to tea about 5.15 p.m. After a talk went down to Aveline's and got a view looking out of the excavation which now extends right down the first slope, the northern half. They are now systematizing excavation and all the entrance outside is squared up.

HILLGROVE 12 August 1921 (Friday)

Reg Balch dropped in soon after 11 a.m. and with three ropes, pulley, bar and gelignite etc. we went over to Hillgrove. Let off a succession of small charges, *bunches* of two, three, four or five cartridges put in the right places, tightly between boulders and well tamped, did a great deal of useful work as compared with larger charges (fired Wednesday) not so well tamped. We hauled out with the ropes and pulley five or six boulders, whole or in fragments, and only stopped for want of more gelignite. Steady blasting and breaking up of boulders one at a time in the (now) main pit, until we come to a visible and possible way down, is I am sure the only satisfactory and possible means of progress. The difficulty now and in 1911 has always been that the exact whereabouts of a passable passage down has never been discovered and one has to keep on making tests. However, by knocking off time at 4 p.m. we had lowered the pit at the very back under earth arch 3 or 4 ft and cleared of all boulders. The whole place now looks far more hopeful. For quick work, sheers across the pit and a differential tackle and plenty of gelignite would be ideal. We solidified my dam made on Monday last and large stones were placed all over the top platform and behind it on mud etc. to prevent superficial washing down for some time to come. We had two more trials at firing the tube, each time blowing off 6 in or so and we then buried it in a rabbit hole in disgust. I feel sure contact was good but probably the charge was too long and contact surfaces too small; also, except for the tin covering the top end could not be really well tamped on either occasion.

SWILDON'S HOLE 13 August 1921 (Saturday)

A visit with visitors for the purpose of lowering pebble dam and fixing large metal chute at head of the 40 ft. In at 11 a.m., Balch, Holly, R. Balch, Higgins, Revd Quinn, Mrs Quinn and friend, Quinn junior and friend, Tratman and another Bristol man. Got good photos of entrance to water rift and stalagmite dam while the others were fixing the chute, which consisted of two sections of 6 in light galvanised tubing which telescoped together. This was fixed in the gully on left at head of 40 ft, cemented round and the forward end suspended to the stalactite above with galvanised wire. This

11 August 1921. Aveline's Hole: Tratman at the excavation in the first slope, with Balch above at the entrance; half-plate

13 August 1921. Swildon's Hole: the stalagmite dam in the water rift showing the enlargement made at the near end, Holly in the stream and Reg Balch in the upper squeeze; half-plate

we hope will take all the water and shoot it out into the pot quite clear of anyone on the ladder below it, even when a fair sized stream is going down. In addition to this, much debris was removed from the stream bed towards far end of rift, and this had the effect of considerably lowering the water level in the squeeze. With stones thrown into the mud at last visit, this was now drier than it had ever been known before. If a board is used through here in future, the passage of it should not be too bad under normal circumstances. They were some time in the rift so I started back with the Quinn party and Higgins, who wanted to get out early. We took the long dry way and for a little while I was confused because I had not remembered that there are *two* small boulder chambers on this route. I was looking for the 'Imp' passage out of the lower one, whereas in fact it runs out of the lower end of the upper one. We got out only a short while in advance of the remainder, who caught us up at the entrance by coming the short dry way.

On Sunday 14 August JHS and Mr Symes took 'a short walk round the old plantation and saw two shafts still quite open, he pointed out to me several others he had himself filled from time to time.' They then went to Priddy minery pool, where Symes pointed out the wall running down from North Hill as being the old boundary line between St Cuthbert's mines on the south side and Chewton minery on the north. Later they met Balch and together went and examined Plantation Swallet, 'he considers now that it does look promising though not before. He

told me the history of the upper tunnelled portion. After the paper mill's lawsuit stopping mine drainage to Wookey Hole, this was started on the sly in this wood, the idea being to conduct superfluous water, a great nuisance, off the workings by a wooden aqueduct. No doubt a small swallet at this point existed previously, showing a likely line of drainage (big natural fissures occur lower down). Work proceeded for some time and then the bottom fell out of the big depression down below on the other side of the wall, a huge pool used to stand here and no doubt water action had been taking place for a long period, thereby creating a new swallet large enough for all the water and the tunnel was abandoned.' JHS took a photograph of the bottom of the tunnel with the 5 in × 4 in camera, then returned to Green Ore with Symes.

Just over a fortnight later, on 2 September, JHS and Doris's first child, Geoffrey, was born.

SWILDON'S HOLE 1 October 1921

After many changes this day was fixed for the photographic expedition, a large party including Bristol men [UBSS members] was organised. At last moment I could not go owing to DES [Doris] returning to Swallowfield the previous day. HEB says 10 hr underground, he got one or two good quarter-plates including Langford [UBSS] crossing Double Pot. No fresh things found.

On 15 October JHS went by train with his father to Wells and took some fine photographs of the Cathedral from Tor Hill and of the reflections in St Andrew's Well. On 12 November there was another major expedition down Swildon's Hole when another exciting discovery was made. This was a richly decorated series of grottoes half-way between Barnes' Loop and the termination, reached by climbing above the active streamway, and which equalled Barnes' Loop in their beauty. Originally named the November 12 (1921) Grottoes, they are now known as Tratman's Temple after their discoverer Edgar Tratman.

SWILDON'S HOLE 12 November 1921

Drought continues, another expedition fixed, strong boxes painted and lined with felt for (1) whole-plate camera and (2) slides, strapped with handles, likewise canvas fans on long bamboos for fumes. O. S. Davies said he would come so took me and Greenhill down in his car, lunching and picking up Bristol rope ladders at Burrington where Dobson, EKT [Tratman] and one other were lunching in hut. They biked on after us and having reached Priddy, we went to Swildon's Hole, followed down by HEB, EKT, Dobber [Dobson] and Bird. Clem Richardson, Cooper and Maltby of Sidcot arrived before we started over and came down in first party which I led.

Entered at 3.30 p.m. and first halt made in grotto where whole party joined up. Water rift still dry and lower passage through water rift dam fairly comfortable. We opened up the camera first at Shrine as three passable half-plates were taken on 1 August between there and the 40 ft. A good whole-plate and half-plate were obtained

with a flash, again the powder was troublesome, not by sparking but by fumes which seemed worse than usual. They travelled down with us and, though fans helped considerably, were not got rid of till the lower side of Double Pot when we got a good half-plate. Next photo was the climb to Barnes' Loop, the wide angle lens I'd borrowed from Bromhead I found afterwards was much slower than my own, and consequently there was underexposure. We climbed into the Loop, the best subjects were not so get-at-able as I had expected, many being overhead. We got a good one of the White Way and pools etc., but as usual photography went slowly; we boiled up the cocoa which was very welcome as we were chilled with much standing about.

Meanwhile Tratman had taken the new-

15 October 1921. Trees and walk along the south side of the Bishop's Palace moat at Wells; whole-plate

12 November 1921. Swildon's Hole: the Shrine, after the 20 ft fall; whole-plate

12 November 1921. Swildon's Hole: lower anchorage for rope over the Double Pot, which is behind the figures of Greenhill and Richardson; half-plate

comers of the party down to the termination [Sump 1], where there was again trouble with the gas from the mud. On turning back, they explored a chimney near the last sharp angle and climbed up an awkward slope into some remarkably fine grottoes (seen today for the first time), finer and more wonderful in some ways than Barnes' Loop. Where the latter is remarkable for its whiteness and massive formations, the former is probably unique to the present for (1) crowded pencils of great length, (2) numerous tall and slender pillars of sentinel type up to 7 ft or over, (3) groups of short pillars more like bosses at one place, (4) a gigantic mound, which if it can be considered a single mass exceeds in circumference the Beehive stalagmite of Lamb Lair. They came back and reported to HEB who was with me in the Loop. He immediately went down with rest of party to see it and was not gone very long. To my great disappointment, my hands being full with the whole-plate, I had to decide to finish up the photos where I was, so I did not get down to see it. I spent perhaps 3 minutes explaining to HEB the working of my crazy old half-plate, he had never handled it before. I had lost count but reckoned there were four or five unexposed, so told him to do four. Results were more than fortunate, he got the four best we had taken that day as results proved afterwards. He was remarkably lucky and of course highly delighted with the place. On his return we packed up our traps. We used magnesium ribbon only after the first effort, although the last trial was a failure owing to fumes from the ribbon.

Much delay at the 40 ft again, we seemed to be there hours and I took the opportunity of getting a whole-plate of the corrugated strata, which shows perhaps at its best not 50 ft away; this came out well. At long last we all got up and arrived at the top all a bit fagged, at last got the ladders up, rolled them and packed them. All gear was finally checked in the water chamber and we slowly progressed up the usual way to the entrance. Dobber and HEB were particularly fagged and the latter, as he lay out at each stage almost dropping asleep, looked decidely picturesque with the seat of his saturated boiler suit torn out and hanging in a mournful manner round his knees, to the no little impediment of his movements. At last we smelt the fresh air again, many feet in we felt it growing colder and when outside found there was a severe frost, everything was snow white. This was at 6.30 a.m. and coming daylight slowly revealed to us its beauties, we could hardly stay to study them for the cold. Mrs Main, an angel in disguise, was up by this time and invited the car party, increased by the addition of Eric Bird, to a cheery kitchen with blazing fire, hot tea and plenty of home-made bread and butter, a veritable godsend. A thoroughly successful expedition.

The last entry for 1921 was also the last diary entry altogether, and was written in note form as if it was just the start of a longer description never completed. It was a visit to Hillgrove just after Christmas.

HILLGROVE 27 December 1921 (Tuesday)

Two Birds and self down by bus 7.40 a.m.

(Bryan and Jack Savory came too, left us at H. doing a day's walk and getting on our return bus before us at Wells). Joined at H. by Balch, Barnes, Sinnock and Wicks.

However, in the MNRC Report for 1921, Balch reported: 'The season has not been allowed to pass without two further attempts to enter the swallet at Hillgrove, where for several years Mr J. H. Savory has persistently attempted to force an entrance. Explosives have been used on both occasions and on the last attempt made on 27 December considerable progress was made. It is probable that we are at last on the verge of an entry into the labyrinth of ways which are indicated by the numerous swallets which here abound.' Sadly this optimistic prediction has never been realised.

28 February 1922. Gough's Cave: the Diamond Stream; half-plate

EPILOGUE

After 1921 only a few further caving exploits by JHS can be identified from dated photographs in his albums. Thus, in 1922, he was photographing again in Gough's Cave at Cheddar on 9 and 28 February, and in Cox's Cave also on the latter date. At Easter he was digging again at the Priddy Pool (now Waldegrave) and Plantation Swallets with the Barnes brothers, Bird brothers and Clem Richardson. On 3 August he went down Swildon's Hole as far as the termination with Balch, Eric Bird, Edgar Tratman and others, and took some good photographs. One of Tratman holding the ladder at the bottom of the 40 ft drop shows a canvas pipe for containing the waterfall, perhaps attached to the metal chute that had been fitted on 13 August 1921. A superb one of the central group of stalagmites in the November 12 (1921) Grottoes is arguably the best caving photograph he ever took. He was certainly sufficiently pleased with it himself to have it enlarged and framed, something he did with only two others, those of the Witch of Wookey and of Balch in Eastwater boulder ruckle. In a letter to Balch, he said of the Swildon's picture:

A topping instance of good *strong* light and shadow got by side lighting from concealed corner – contrasts are fine. Pity pillar on extreme right didn't come in to balance composition, but that would have brought your corner in as well where light was coming from. Water evidently got into camera by its fall in pool – it pulled a square half inch of film off this subject, can you spot it? I can only attribute this to the film sticking here to the sheath in front.

The same photograph featured in Balch's 15th Annual Report of the MNRC, published in the WNHAS *Proceedings* for 1922.

In 1923 JHS's parents moved back to Clifton to live, and JHS started to build a house on land bought by his father at the end of Church Road in Abbots Leigh. The house, Windyridge, was built with the help of local craftsmen, and was eventually ready for JHS and his family to move into on Christmas Eve. Clearly the building would have taken most of JHS's spare time, but there are photographs of Hillgrove Swallet at Easter, of a rock shelter and bones, labelled '21.4.23 Walton', and of a caving party of ten, including Doris and Bryan Savory, at Swildon's Hole on 8 September. An illustrated lecture entitled 'The Lime-

3 August 1922. Swildon's Hole: Tratman steadying the ladder at the foot of the 40 ft drop, showing a canvas pipe for containing the waterfall- half-plate

3 August 1922. Swildon's Hole: entrance to the November 12 1921 Grotto (now Tratman's Temple) from inside; half-plate

3 August 1922. Swildon's Hole: the cairn at the lowest termination (now Sump One), JHS, Balch and Bird; half-plate (with candle track)

stone Caves, Underground Rivers and Gorges of Mendip', which JHS gave to the Bath and District Branch of the Somerset Archaeological and Natural History Society, was printed in full in the Society's 1923 *Proceedings*.

There was only one identifiable project in 1924, when JHS and Paul Sinnock, helped by Bryan Savory, excavated and surveyed the Tickenham Rock Shelter 'on Mr Burleton's Holding, Elton Estate, Clevedon', JHS's survey being dated 27 August. In 1925 JHS and Doris's second child, Philippa, was born in May, and on 15 August, with a party which included Balch, Bird and Tratman, JHS took several photographs in the upper series of Swildon's Hole. Some of these make interesting comparison with almost identical pictures taken twelve and fourteen years previously. He was at the Priddy Fair and at Lamb Lair again in August of the same year. The *Mendip Cave Guide* (1977 edition) states that JHS dug at Waldegrave (Priddy Pool) Swallet in 1925–6, and two undated photogaphs of him and Clem Richardson at that swallet could well have been taken then. There is one of Doris at Hillgrove in August 1926, but nothing for 1927. The last caving photographs of all were a series of whole-plates taken at Wookey Hole on two days in March 1928, showing the cave entrance and source of the Axe from outside, the first chamber with a boat in it, and good ones of the Index Grotto in the W. series. This may have been part of a collaborative project with his artist friend John Hassall, because in the same year Hassall produced some fine paintings of just the scenes that JHS had photographed. Pre-

sumably these had been commissioned, because they were used for postcards published by the then owner of Wookey Hole Cave, Captain G. W. Hodgkinson.

In his biography of Balch, *Pioneer Under the Mendips*, William Stanton writes:

Returning to 1928, in that year for the first time in half a decade, Balch recorded an attempt to revisit lower Swildon's. (It seems, however, that trips to Sump 1 were regularly made by other MNRC men and by the UBSS). Perhaps stimulated by a lecture on Irish caves by Dr. Baker earlier in the year, he and Harry Savory concocted a devilish scheme to denaturise the mud choke at Sump 1, and its surroundings. Tratman tells of a UBSS party that, arriving on Priddy Green for a joint trip, found these two gentlemen guarding a large home-made bomb consisting of a four foot length of iron pipe stuffed with explosive. Lengths of fuse stuck out of holes bored at intervals, indicating that the detonators were already in place. Posterity may regret that the UBSS men refused to have anything to do with the bomb, which languished on the Green while the party were below. (It must be added that the young men may have underestimated their elders. Savory's friend Clement Richardson writes: 'Please delete Savory's name from association with a dangerous home-made explosive affair. Savory as a Royal Engineer was competent with his explosives.') Balch briefly records the plan as follows: 'We intended to penetrate to the bottom of Swildon's Hole and remove the mud

Easter 1923. The main feeder stream for Hillgrove Swallet running strongly, E. and G. Bird; half-plate

Easter 1923. JHS at the dig at Hillgrove Swallet; plate 5 in × 4 in

27 March 1928. Wookey Hole: River Axe in the first chamber, JHS on the right; whole-plate

barrier that bars the way, but, the water preventing access, we spent our energies in blowing away one of the most tiresome hindrances to exploration, the small creep in the Water Rift. Here, where hitherto a tiny hole has been the only possible passage, we fired two charges and have made free a passage that will never be blocked by debris again. Probably at least an hour will be saved on every future trip into the deeper parts of this great cave.'

JHS retained his interest in caving and his membership of the MNRC, WNHAS and Somerset Archaeological and Natural History Society for the rest of his life. He and his brother Mortimer continued to run Savorys printing company jointly after their father's death in 1936, and throughout the 1920s and 1930s he travelled abroad regularly on business. Most of these trips were to Holland, where he developed close friendships with customers, and where he often stayed to study the country and its customs, to sketch, and to observe and photograph its rich birdlife. By applying the same attention to detail, and usually waiting patiently in a hide for the right moment, he soon became as successful at photographing birds as he had been with caves. As well as in Holland, he took many photographs of nesting birds in the Abbots Leigh area and elsewhere in Somerset, and later of various seabirds on islands such as Lundy, Grassholm and Steep Holm. He rejoined the Bristol Naturalists' Society in 1931, and was President of its Ornithological Section in 1933, 1935–8 and 1945–7. He was also Vice-President of the parent Society in 1935–6

and 1949–50, President in 1954–5; and was largely instrumental in 1955 in obtaining Council's approval for the formation of the Junior Section, of which he was Chairman of the adult Advisory Committee. On the foundation of the Steep Holm Trust in 1953, he represented the Society in negotiations for the lease of the island and undertook the dual office of Chairman and Secretary of the Trust. His services to the Society were recognised by his election in 1962 as an Honorary Member. In addition, he was a keen supporter of the Lundy Field Society from its earliest days, he joined the Wildfowl Trust soon after its inception, and was a founder member of the Gloucestershire Trust for Nature Conservation.

In 1930 JHS was invited to take part in a hawking holiday at Avebury together with the brothers Charles and Hugh Knight and a few other falconers. There he met for the first time George Edward Lodge, the well-known veteran wildlife artist whose particular interests were falconry and birds of prey, and with whom JHS maintained a close friendship until Lodge's death in 1954. JHS soon acquired his own birds, peregrines, goshawks and sparrowhawks, became a member of the British Falconers' Club, and attended their summer gatherings at Avebury until 1935, after which he remained a member but ceased hawking actively. As well as George Lodge, he became acquainted with other bird artists, notably J. A. Shepherd, R. B. Talbot Kelly, Eric Ennion and Peter Scott, in connection with commissions for Savorys' greetings cards. Among his other interests, he was a Council member of the Royal West of

19 May 1933. Avocet approaching nest, Hook of Holland

June 1932. Whitethroat, Abbots Leigh, Somerset

England Academy, a life member of the Bristol Savages, a member of the Royal Commonwealth and Anglo–Netherlands Societies, and a loyal Old Cliftonian, whose shooting team he captained at annual matches against the School. Throughout his adult life he lectured regularly to various organisations on topics ranging from Mendip Caves and West Country Archaeology to Dutch Customs, Islands, Birds, Bird Lore and Falconry.

Of his former caving companions, JHS kept in closest touch with Herbert Balch. Balch had started his career with the Post Office in Wells as a telegram boy and rose to become local postmaster in 1928; apparently this appointment would have come sooner if he had been prepared to leave Wells. On his retirement in 1931, he took over the full-time curatorship of Wells Museum, which he had founded in 1895, and he and his wife moved to live in its new premises at No. 8, Cathedral Green, where it still is today, while continuing to use their railway carriage retreat at Rookham. As well as his earlier collaborative books, *The Netherworld of Mendip* with E. A. Baker (1907) and *Wookey Hole, Its Caves and Cave Dwellers* with JHS (1914), he also wrote *The Caves of Mendip* (1926), *The Great Cave of Wookey Hole* (1929), *Cheddar, Its Gorge and Caves* (1935) and *Mendip, Its Swallet Caves and Rock Shelters* (1937). The last three were combined in a single volume, *The Mendip Caves*, in 1948. In recognition of his services to the City of Wells, he was made an Honorary Freeman in 1944.

In his old age, Balch continued to take a lively interest in all MNRC activities, and personally remained in command of excavations at Badger Hole, where he would spend Saturday afternoons at the sorting table. JHS was photographed with him there in 1954, the year he finally retired from the museum curatorship, aged eighty-four. His wife died shortly afterwards and he went to live with his daughter Margaret on the other side of Wells. He was still Chairman of the MNRC, and on the day after the Committee's (50th) jubilee AGM and dinner at the Star Hotel on 7 January 1956, he wrote to JHS:

My dear Harry,

It was a very fine gathering of the MNRC last night, though I could not reach to speak to you, as the fleshpots called louder than the friendly chats. I could not venture the chair at the supper for hours on end, and was far better away, to my great regret. However do please lose no chance of calling on me – any time, any day. Love to you and yours, always a happy memory, to remain as long as life lasts, and who knows, beyond. Yours sincerely, Herbert. Please imagine all I would have said to you.

Balch died in his sleep on 27 May 1958.

In November 1961, a richly decorated cave was exposed during quarrying at Fairy Cave Quarry, and was named Balch Cave in his honour. I was fortunate in being able to visit this cave soon afterwards, in May 1962, when I photographed some of the formations there. Sadly, many of these were destroyed later and much of the cave was removed by quarrying.

August 1932. JHS with a goshawk, Avebury; (Evening World)

1954. JHS and Herbert Balch at the Badger Hole, Wookey Hole

May 1962. In Erratic Passage, Balch Cave
(John Savory)

In October 1939, just a month after war was declared, Doris Savory died after a long illness. The family continued living at Windyridge, however, where they were joined by Mortimer Savory, who moved out from Bristol. Geoffrey joined the Navy and in January 1941 JHS married Dorothy Boorne, a family friend who had nursed Doris during the last months of her life. From May 1940 until the end of 1944, JHS and Mortimer together commanded the Abbots Leigh unit of the local Home Guard, which had its HQ at Windyridge. In August 1943 I was born, the only child from JHS's second marriage.

Savorys printing company continued to operate at its Park Row premises throughout World War II, although it was damaged during a night-time bombing raid when half a tombstone from nearby St Michael's graveyard fell through its roof! The Company had established a reputation for producing first-rate material, but after the war its success began to wane in the face of competition from larger companies who could afford to install the latest improved machinery necessary for mass production. Eventually, the firm moved from Park Row into offices in Nelson Street, where it operated on a small scale before finally closing down when JHS retired in 1958. Its sister company, Vandycks, also closed at about the same time.

JHS and Dorothy had moved from Abbots Leigh to live in Redland, Bristol in 1951, and during his retirement he made regular visits with parties to Steep Holm and also carried on a project started by the Revd F.L. Blathwayt, of locating and describing former duck decoy sites in Somerset. When a cousin of mine, Dick Savory's son Robert, and I were, successively, involved in Mendip caving with a Clifton College caving club, he provided encouragement and assistance for our activities, with friendly advice, transport and lectures at the School. He died after a short illness on 25 June 1962, two months before his seventy-third birthday, and was buried in the family grave at Abbots Leigh.

9 February 1922. Gough's Cave: Aladdin's Grotto reflected; half-plate

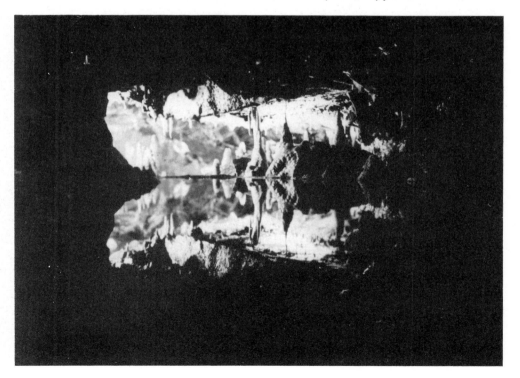

27 March 1928. Wookey Hole: the Index Grotto, west series; whole-plate

INDEX